The Angry Monkey

The Angry Monkey

A Story in Simplified Chinese and Pinyin,
1800 Word Vocabulary Level

Book 19 of the *Journey to the West* Series

Written by Jeff Pepper
Chinese Translation by Xiao Hui Wang

Based on chapters 56 through 58 of the original Chinese novel *Journey to the West* by Wu Cheng'en

Published in the United States by Imagin8 Press LLC, Verona, Pennsylvania, US. For information, contact us via email at info@imagin8press.com, or visit www.imagin8press.com.

Our books may be purchased directly in quantity at a reduced price, visit our website www.imagin8press.com for details.

Written by Jeff Pepper
Chinese translation by Xiao Hui Wang
Cover design by Katelyn Pepper and Jeff Pepper
Book design by Jeff Pepper
Artwork by Next Mars Media, Luoyang, China
Audiobook narration by Junyou Chen

Based on the original 16th century Chinese novel by Wu Cheng'en, and the unabridged four-volume translation by Anthony C. Yu, University of Chicago Press, 2012 (revised edition)

ISBN: 978-1952601675
Version 02c

Acknowledgements

We are deeply indebted to the late Anthony C. Yu for his incredible four-volume translation, *The Journey to the West* (1983, revised 2012, University of Chicago Press). Many thanks to the team at Next Mars Media for their terrific illustrations, and Junyou Chen for narrating the audiobook.

We're also grateful to Jim McClanahan[1] and H.L. Lam[2] for their insights into this story and the nature of the six-eared macaque.

Audiobook

A complete Chinese language audio version of this book is available free of charge. To access it, go to YouTube.com and search for the Imagin8 Press channel. There you will find free audiobooks for this and all the other books in this series.

You can also visit our website, www.imagin8press.com, to find a direct link to the YouTube audiobook, as well as information about our other books.

---

[1] McClanahan, J. (2020). "Origin of the Six-Eared Macaque and the Character's Influence on Black Myth, Wukong." In the blog "Journey to the West Research," journeytothewestresearch.com/2020/11/04/origin-of-the-six-eared-macaque-and-the-characters-influence-on-black-myth-wukong/.

[2] Lam, H. L. (2005). "Cannibalizing the Heart, The Politics of Allegory and The Journey to the West." In E. Ziolkowski (Ed.). *Literature, Religion, and East/West Comparison* (pp. 162-178). Newark, University of Delaware Press.

Preface

Here's a summary of the events of the previous books in the Journey to the West *series. The numbers in brackets indicate in which book in the series the events occur.*

Thousands of years ago, in a magical version of ancient China, a small stone monkey is born on Flower Fruit Mountain. Hatched from a stone egg, he spends his early years playing with other monkeys. They follow a stream to its source and discover a secret room behind a waterfall. This becomes their home, and the stone monkey becomes their king. After several years the stone monkey begins to worry about the impermanence of life. One of his companions tells him that certain great sages are exempt from the wheel of life and death. The monkey goes in search of these great sages, meets one and studies with him, and receives the name Sun Wukong. He develops remarkable magical powers, and when he returns to Flower Fruit Mountain he uses these powers to save his troop of monkeys from a ravenous monster. *[Book 1]*

With his powers and his confidence increasing, Sun Wukong manages to offend the underwater Dragon King, the Dragon King's mother, all ten Kings of the Underworld, and the great Jade Emperor himself. Finally, goaded by a couple of troublemaking demons, he goes too far, calling himself the Great Sage Equal to Heaven and sets events in motion that cause him some serious trouble. *[Book 2]*

Trying to keep Sun Wukong out of trouble, the Jade Emperor gives him a job in heaven taking care of his Garden of Immortal Peaches, but the monkey cannot stop himself from eating all the peaches. He impersonates a great Immortal and crashes a party in Heaven, stealing the guests' food and drink and barely escaping to his loyal troop of monkeys back on

Earth. In the end he battles an entire army of Immortals and men, and discovers that even calling himself the Great Sage Equal to Heaven does not make him equal to everyone in Heaven. As punishment, the Buddha himself imprisons him under a mountain. *[Book 3]*

Five hundred years later, the Buddha decides it is time to bring his wisdom to China, and he needs someone to lead the journey. A young couple undergo a terrible ordeal around the time of the birth of their child Xuanzang. The boy grows up as an orphan but at age eighteen he learns his true identity, avenges the death of his father and is reunited with his mother. Xuanzang will later fulfill the Buddha's wish and lead the journey to the west. *[Book 4]*

Another storyline starts innocently enough, with two good friends chatting as they walk home after eating and drinking at a local inn. One of the men, a fisherman, tells his friend about a fortuneteller who advises him on where to find fish. This seemingly harmless conversation between two minor characters triggers a series of events that eventually cost the life of a supposedly immortal being, and cause the great Tang Emperor himself to be dragged down to the underworld. He is released by the Ten Kings of the Underworld, but is trapped in hell and only escapes with the help of a deceased courtier. *[Book 5]*

Barely making it back to the land of the living, the Emperor selects the young monk Xuanzang to undertake the journey, after being strongly influenced by the great bodhisattva Guanyin. The young monk sets out on his journey. After many difficulties his path crosses that of Sun Wukong, and the monk releases him from his prison under a mountain. Sun Wukong becomes the monk's first disciple. *[Book 6]*

As their journey gets underway, they encounter a mysterious

river-dwelling dragon, then run into serious trouble while staying in the temple of a 270 year old abbot. Their troubles deepen when they meet the abbot's friend, a terrifying black bear monster, and Sun Wukong must defend his master. *[Book 7]*

The monk, now called Tangseng, acquires two more disciples. The first is the pig-man Zhu Bajie, the embodiment of stupidity, laziness, lust and greed. In his previous life, Zhu was the Marshal of the Heavenly Reeds, responsible for the Jade Emperor's entire navy and 80,000 sailors. Unable to control his appetites, he got drunk at a festival and attempted to seduce the Goddess of the Moon. The Jade Emperor banished him to earth, but as he plunged from heaven to earth he ended up in the womb of a sow and was reborn as a man-eating pig monster. He was married to a farmer's daughter, but fights with Sun Wukong and ends up joining and becoming the monk's second disciple. *[Book 8]*

Sha Wujing was once the Curtain Raising Captain but was banished from heaven by the Yellow Emperor for breaking an extremely valuable cup during a drunken visit to the Peach Festival. The travelers meet Sha and he joins them as Tangseng's third and final disciple. The four pilgrims arrive at a beautiful home seeking a simple vegetarian meal and a place to stay for the night. What they encounter instead is a lovely and wealthy widow and her three even more lovely daughters. This meeting is, of course, much more than it appears to be, and it turns into a test of commitment and virtue for all of the pilgrims, especially for the lazy and lustful pig-man Zhu Bajie. *[Book 9]*

Heaven continues to put more obstacles in their path. They arrive at a secluded mountain monastery which turns out to be the home of a powerful master Zhenyuan and an ancient and magical ginseng tree. As usual, the travelers' search for a nice hot meal and a place to sleep quickly turns into a disaster. Zhenyuan has gone away for a few days and has left his two youngest disciples in charge. They welcome the travelers, but soon there are misunderstandings, arguments, battles in the sky, and before long the travelers are facing a powerful and extremely angry adversary, as well as mysterious magic fruits and a large frying pan full of hot oil. *[Book 10]*

Next, Tangseng and his band of disciples come upon a strange pagoda in a mountain forest. Inside they discover the fearsome Yellow Robed Monster who is living a quiet life with his wife and their two children. Unfortunately the monster has a bad habit of ambushing and eating travelers. The travelers find themselves drawn into a story of timeless love and complex lies as they battle for survival against the monster and his allies. *[Book 11]*

The travelers arrive at level Top Mountain and encounter their most powerful adversaries yet: Great King Golden Horn and his younger brother Great King Silver Horn. These two monsters, assisted by their elderly mother and hundreds of well-armed demons, attempt to capture and liquefy Sun Wukong, and eat the Tang monk and his other disciples. *[Book 12]*

The monk and his disciples resume their journey. They stop to rest at a mountain monastery in Black Rooster Kingdom, and Tangseng is visited in a dream by someone claiming to be the ghost of a murdered king. Is he telling the truth or is he actually a demon in disguise? Sun Wukong offers to sort things out with his iron rod. But things do not go as planned. *[Book 13]*

While traveling the Silk Road, Tangseng and his three disciples encounter a young boy hanging upside down from a tree. They rescue him only to discover that he is really Red Boy, a powerful and malevolent demon and, it turns out, Sun Wukong's nephew. The three disciples battle the demon but soon discover that he can produce deadly fire and smoke which nearly kills Sun Wukong. *[Book 14]*

leaving Red Boy with the bodhisattva Guanyin, the travelers continue to the wild country west of China. They arrive at a strange city where Daoism is revered and Buddhism is forbidden. Sun Wukong gleefully causes trouble in the city, and finds himself in a series of deadly competitions with three Daoist Immortals. *[Book 15]*

Continuing westward, The Monkey King Sun Wukong leads the Tang monk and his two fellow disciples westward until they come to a village where the people live in fear of the Great Demon King who demands two human sacrifices each year. Sun Wukong and the pig-man Zhu Bajie try to trick the Demon King but soon discover that the Demon King has clever plans of his own. *[Book 16]*

Several months later, Sun Wukong steals rice from an elderly villager's kitchen, then Zhu Bajie takes three silk vests from a seemingly abandoned tower. These small crimes trigger a violent confrontation with a monster who uses a strange and powerful weapon to disarm and defeat the disciples. Helpless and out of options, Sun Wukong must journey to Thunderclap Mountain and beg the Buddha himself for help. *[Book 17]*

Springtime comes and the travelers run into difficulties and temptations in a nation of women and girls. First, Tangseng and Zhu become pregnant after drinking from the Mother and Child River. Later, the nation's queen meets Tangseng and pressures him to marry her. He barely escapes that fate, only to be kidnapped by a powerful female demon who takes him to her cave and tries to seduce him. The travelers must use all their tricks and strength to escape. *[Book 18]*

After defeating the demon, they continue on their journey to the west…

The Angry Monkey

愤怒的猴子

Dì 56 Zhāng

Qīn'ài de háizi, jīntiān wǎnshàng wǒ yào gěi nǐ jiǎng lìng yígè guānyú héshang Tángsēng hé tā de sān gè túdì de gùshì. Sān gè túdì shì hóu wáng Sūn Wùkōng, zhū rén Zhū Bājiè, ānjìng qiángdà de Shā Wùjìng. Nǐ jìdé zuótiān wǎnshàng de gùshì, tāmen cóng xiēzi yāoguài de dòng lǐ táo le chūlái. Ránhòu, tāmen jìxù tāmen de xīyóu, qù qǔ shèngjīng, dài huí Táng dìguó.

Chūntiān biàn chéng le xiàtiān. Yóurénmen yánzhe Sīchóu Zhīlù màn màn de xiàng xī zǒu. Tāmen kàndào huángsè de niǎo zài tāmen de tóu shàng fēi, zài wēnnuǎn de qīng fēng zhōng tāmen kěyǐ wéndào huāxiāng.

Zǎo xià de yìtiān, tāmen lái dào le yízuò dàshān. Shānlù xiàngshàng, biàn dé gèng kùnnán. Tāmen pá shàng shān. Kōngqì biàn liáng le. Tāmen kàndào le shānlù liǎngbiān de huāngyě dòngwù. Hěn yuǎn de dìfāng, tāmen tīng dào lǎohǔ de páoxiāo shēng.

Jīngguò jǐ gè xiǎoshí de páshān, tāmen lái dào le shāndǐng, kāishǐ zài xī miàn xiàng shānxià zǒu qù. Tángsēng de mǎ lèi le, kāishǐ zǒu dé màn le. Tángsēng bùnéng ràng mǎ zǒu dé gèng kuài yìxiē. Zhū duì tā dà

第 56 章

亲爱的孩子，今天晚上我要给你讲另一个关于和尚唐僧和他的三个徒弟的故事。三个徒弟是猴王孙悟空、猪人猪八戒、安静强大的沙悟净。你记得昨天晚上的故事，他们从蝎子妖怪的洞里逃了出来。然后，他们继续他们的西游，去取圣经，带回唐帝国。

春天变成了夏天。游人们沿着丝绸之路慢慢地向西走。他们看到黄色的鸟在他们的头上飞，在温暖的轻风中他们可以闻到花香。

早夏的一天，他们来到了一座大山。山路向上，变得更困难。他们爬上山。空气变凉了。他们看到了山路两边的荒野动物。很远的地方，他们听到老虎的咆哮声。

经过几个小时的爬山，他们来到了山顶，开始在西面向山下走去。唐僧的马累了，开始走得慢了。唐僧不能让马走得更快一些。猪对它大

hǎn, dàn mǎ bù lǐ tā. Sūn Wùkōng shuō, "ràng wǒ lái ba." Tā duì mǎ huīzhe tā de Jīn Gū Bàng, duìzhe tā dà hǎn. Mǎshàng, mǎ kāishǐ pǎo le qǐlái. Táng héshang xià huài le, shuāngshǒu jǐn jǐn zhuā zhù mǎ. Mǎ pǎo le èrshí lǐ, bǎ Tángsēng dài dào hěn qiánmiàn, lí sān gè túdì hěn yuǎn. Zhōngyú, mǎ lái dào le píngdì. Tā bù pǎo le, yòu kāishǐ xíngzǒu.

Zài mǎ pǎo de shíhòu, Tángsēng yǐjīng hěn hàipà le. Dāng mǎ zài yícì kāishǐ xíngzǒu shí, tā fàngsōng le xiàlái, tái qǐtóu lái. Zài lù de qiánmiàn, tā kàndào sānshí jǐ gè rén zhàn zài lùshàng. Tāmen dōu názhe jiàn, máo hé cháng bàng. Qízhōng yígè nánrén zhǎngzhe lǜ liǎn, cháng yá, kàn shàngqù jiù xiàng shì yìtiáo qiángdà de lóng. Lìng yígè shì hóng tóufà, dà yǎnjīng, kàn qǐlái xiàng yì zhī fènnù de lǎohǔ. Tángsēng kànchū tāmen shì qiángdào.

"Nǐ yào qù nǎlǐ?" Lǜ liǎn qiángdào shǒulǐng wèn. "Wǒmen bùxiǎng shānghài nǐ, wǒmen zhǐ xiǎng yào nǐ de guòlù qián. Mǎshàng bǎ tā gěi wǒ!"

喊，但马不理他。孙悟空说，“让我来吧。”他对马挥着他的金箍棒，对着它大喊。马上，马开始跑了起来。唐和尚吓坏了，双手紧紧抓住马。马跑了二十里，把唐僧带到很前面，离三个徒弟很远。终于，马来到了平地。它不跑了，又开始行走。

在马跑的时候，唐僧已经很害怕了。当马再一次开始行走时，他放松了下来，抬起头来。在路的前面，他看到三十几个人站在路上。他们都拿着剑、矛和长棒。其中一个男人长着绿脸，长牙，看上去就像是一条强大的龙。另一个是红头发，大眼睛，看起来像一只愤怒的老虎。唐僧看出他们是强盗。

“你要去哪里？”绿脸强盗首领[3]问。“我们不想伤害你，我们只想要你的过路钱。马上把它给我！”

---

[3] 首领 shǒulǐng – chief

Tángsēng cóng mǎshàng xiàlái. Tā bǎ liǎng shǒuzhǎng fàng zài yìqǐ, ránhòu shuō, "dàwángmen, zhège qióng héshang yǐjīng xíngzǒu duōnián le. Hěnjiǔ yǐqián, wǒ líkāi le Táng guó. Wǒ yào qù xītiān qǔ shèngjīng. Dāng wǒ kāishǐ wǒ de lǚtú shí, wǒ yǒu yìxiē qián, dàn wǒ hěnjiǔ yǐqián jiù yòng wán le. Dàwángmen, wǒ qǐngqiú nǐmen, gěi yìdiǎn réncí, ràng wǒ jìxù wǒ de lǚtú."

Qiángdào shǒulǐng shuō, "Wǒmen shǒuwèizhe zhè tiáo lù, nǐ yào fù qián gěi wǒmen. Rúguǒ nǐ méi qián, jiù gěi wǒmen nǐ de yīfú hé nǐ de mǎ. Nà wǒmen jiù ràng nǐ guòqù."

"Zhè jiàn cháng yī jiù le, yě chuān huài le. Tā shì cóng xǔduō bùtóng de rén nàlǐ yào lái de bù zuò de. Rúguǒ nǐ cóng wǒ zhèlǐ ná zǒu tā, jiù xiàng shā le wǒ yíyàng. Nà shí nǐ huì zěnyàng? Nǐ zhè yìshēng kěnéng shì ge dàwáng, dànshì nǐ de xià yìshēng huílái kěnéng shì yígè dòngwù."

Zhè ràng qiángdào shǒulǐng hěn shēngqì. Tā kāishǐ yòng tā de bàng dǎ hé

唐僧从马上下来。他把两手掌[4]放在一起，然后说，“大王们，这个穷和尚已经行走多年了。很久以前，我离开了唐国。我要去西天取圣经。当我开始我的旅途时，我有一些钱，但我很久以前就用完了。大王们，我请求你们，给一点仁慈，让我继续我的旅途。”

强盗首领说，“我们守卫着这条路，你要付钱给我们。如果你没钱，就给我们你的衣服和你的马。那我们就让你过去。”

“这件长衣旧了，也穿坏了。它是从许多不同的人那里要来的布做的。如果你从我这里拿走它，就像杀了我一样。那时你会怎样？你这一生可能是个大王，但是你的下一生回来可能是一个动物。”

这让强盗首领很生气。他开始用他的棒打和

[4] 手掌　　shǒuzhǎng – palm

shang. Dāng bàng xiàng yǔdiǎn yíyàng dǎ zài tā de tóu shàng shí, Tángsēng yǒu le yígè zhǔyì. Tā shuō, "Qǐng búyào dǎ wǒ. Wǒ yǒu yígè niánqīng de túdì, jǐ fēnzhōng hòu jiù huì dào zhèlǐ. Tā yǒu yì xiǎo dài yínzi. Wǒ huì ràng tā bǎ yínzi gěi nǐ." Qiángdàomen bú zài dǎ Tángsēng. Tāmen bǎ tā bǎng qǐlái, diào zài shù shàng.

Bù yīhuǐ'er, sān míng túdì zǒu jìn le. Zhū kànjiàn Tángsēng diào zài yì kē shù shàng. "Kàn," tā shuō, "wǒmen de shīfu xiǎng yào ràng wǒmen kàn kàn tā yǒu duōme de qiángdà, suǒyǐ tā pá shàng le yì kē shù."

Sūn Wùkōng yòng tā de zuànshí yǎnjīng, bǎ qíngkuàng kàn qīngchǔ le. "Nǐ shì ge bèn rén," tā duì Zhū shuō. "Bié shuō le. Děng zài zhèlǐ. Wǒ qù kàn kàn shì shénme shì." Tā tiào shàng yízuò xiǎoshān, yòu kàn le kàn. Xiànzài tā kàndào le qiángdào. Tā duì zìjǐ shuō, "A, zhè hěn hǎo. Shēngyì lái wǒjiā ménkǒu le!"

Tā yáo le yíxià tā de shēntǐ, biàn chéng le yígè shíliù suì zuǒyòu de niánqīng héshang. Tā zǒu dào Tángsēng miànqián, shuō, "Shīfu,

尚。当棒像雨点[5]一样打在他的头上时，唐僧有了一个主意。他说，“请不要打我。我有一个年轻的徒弟，几分钟后就会到这里。他有一小袋银子。我会让他把银子给你。”强盗们不再打唐僧。他们把他绑起来，吊在树上。

不一会儿，三名徒弟走近了。猪看见唐僧吊在一棵树上。“看，”他说，“我们的师父想要让我们看看他有多么的强大，所以他爬上了一棵树。”

孙悟空用他的钻石眼睛，把情况看清楚了。“你是个笨人，”他对猪说。“别说了。等在这里。我去看看是什么事。”他跳上一座小山，又看了看。现在他看到了强盗。他对自己说，“啊，这很好。生意来我家门口了！”

他摇了一下他的身体，变成了一个十六岁左右的年轻和尚。他走到唐僧面前，说，“师父，

---

5 雨点 yǔdiǎn – raindrops

zhèlǐ fāshēng le shénme shì? Zhèxiē huàirén shì shuí?"

Tángsēng kūzhe shuō, "Wùkōng, qiú nǐ jiù jiù wǒ! Zhèxiē shì fēicháng huài de rén. Tāmen shì qiángdào. Tāmen xiǎng yào wǒ de qián, dànshì dāngrán wǒ méiyǒu shéme kěyǐ gěi tāmen. Suǒyǐ wǒ gàosù tāmen nǐ huì lái. Wǒ shuō nǐ huì gěi tāmen yínzi."

"Nǐ wèishénme gàosù tāmen nàxiē?"

"Wǒ xūyào ràng tāmen tíngzhǐ dǎ wǒ!"

"Hǎo ba, hǎo ba. Wǒ xǐhuān zhège. Rúguǒ nǐ yìzhí zhèyàng zuò, lǎo hóuzi jiù huì yǒu hěnduō shēngyì!"

Shuōhuà de shíhòu, qiángdàomen qiāoqiāo de zài Sūn Wùkōng de sìzhōu wéi le yì quān. Lǜ liǎn qiángdào shǒulǐng shuō, "Xiǎo héshang, nǐ shīfu shuō nǐ yǒu yìdiǎn qián. Bǎ tā gěi wǒmen ba."

"Méi wèntí, wǒ yǒu bù shǎo de jīn hé yín. Dànshì nǐ bìxū xiān ràng wǒ shīfu líkāi." Qiángdào shǒulǐng diǎn le diǎn tóu, jǐ rén bǎ Tángsēng fàng le xiàlái. Héshang pǎo xiàng tā de báimǎ, tiào shàng mǎ,

这里发生了什么事？这些坏人是谁？”

唐僧哭着说，“悟空，求你救救我！这些是非常坏的人。他们是强盗。他们想要我的钱，但是当然我没有什么可以给他们。所以我告诉他们你会来。我说你会给他们银子。”

“你为什么告诉他们那些？”

“我需要让他们停止打我！”

“好吧，好吧。我喜欢这个。如果你一直这样做，老猴子就会有很多生意！”

说话的时候，强盗们悄悄[6]地在孙悟空的四周围了一圈。绿脸强盗首领说，“小和尚，你师父说你有一点钱。把它给我们吧。”

“没问题，我有不少的金和银。但是你必须先让我师父离开。”强盗首领点了点头，几人把唐僧放了下来。和尚跑向他的白马，跳上马，

---

[6] 悄悄　　qiāoqiāo – quietly

fēikuài de qí zǒu le. Sūn Wùkōng zhǔnbèi gēnzhe tā.

Qiángdào shǒulǐng dǎngzhù tā, shuō, “Nǐ xiǎng yào qù nǎlǐ?”

Sūn Wùkōng shuō, “Hǎo ba, wǒ huì zài zhèlǐ duō liú yīhuǐ'er. Dànshì wǒ rènwéi guòlù qián yīnggāi fēnchéng sān fèn.”

Qiángdào shǒulǐng xiàozhe shuō, “A, nǐ zhēnshi ge cōngmíng de xiǎo héshang! Nǐ xiǎng yào liú yìxiē qián gěi zìjǐ, èn? Nà hǎo ba. Bǎ nǐ suǒyǒu de qián dōu gěi wǒmen, wǒmen huì huán gěi nǐ yìdiǎndiǎn. Nǐ kěyǐ bǎ tā cáng zài nǐ de cháng yī lǐ, nǐ de shīfu yǒngyuǎn bú huì zhīdào.”

“Wǒ búshì zhège yìsi.” Sūn Wùkōng huídá. “Wǒ de yìsi shì, bǎ nǐmen cóng qítā yóurén nàlǐ ná de qián dōu ná chūlái. Wǒmen bǎ nà qián fēnchéng sān fèn, liǎng fèn gěi wǒ, yí fèn gěi nǐmen.”

Zhè ràng qiángdàomen fēicháng shēngqì. Tāmen kāishǐ xiàng yǔdiǎn yíyàng dǎ zài Sūn Wùkōng de tóu shàng. Sūn Wùkōng zhǐshì zhànzhe bú dòng. Zhèxiē gōngjī yì diǎn dōu méiyǒu yǐngxiǎng tā. Zuìhòu tā shuō, “Nǐmen jiéshù le ma? Xiànzài wǒ gěi nǐmen kàn yìxiē dōngxi.” Tā cóng ěr

飞快地骑走了。孙悟空准备跟着他。

强盗首领挡住他，说，“你想要去哪里？”

孙悟空说，“好吧，我会在这里多留一会儿。但是我认为过路钱应该分成三份。”

强盗首领笑着说，“啊，你真是个聪明的小和尚！你想要留一些钱给自己，嗯？那好吧。把你所有的钱都给我们，我们会还给你一点点。你可以把它藏在你的长衣里，你的师父永远不会知道。”

“我不是这个意思。”孙悟空回答。“我的意思是，把你们从其他游人那里拿的钱都拿出来。我们把那钱分成三份，两份给我，一份给你们。”

这让强盗们非常生气。他们开始像雨点一样打在孙悟空的头上。孙悟空只是站着不动。这些攻击一点都没有影响他。最后他说，“你们结束了吗？现在我给你们看一些东西。”他从耳

hòu qǔchū yì gēn xiǎo zhēn, ná zài shǒuzhōng."Biàn!" Tā xiǎoshēng shuō. Zhēn mǎshàng biàn chéng le tā de Jīn Gū Bàng, shíliù chǐ cháng, xiàng fànwǎn yíyàng cū.

Tā bǎ bàng fàng zài dìshàng, shuō, "Rúguǒ nǐmen zhōng rènhé rén néng ná qǐ zhè gēn bàng, nǐmen jiù kěyǐ liúzhe tā." Liǎng gè qiángdào shǒulǐng xiǎng yào ná qǐ tā, dànshì jiù xiàng shì cāngyíng xiǎng yào ná qǐ yízuò shān. Zhè shì yīnwèi zhè bàng zhòng yí wàn sānqiān wǔbǎi jīn. Sūn Wùkōng ná qǐ bàng, shuō, "Xiànzài wǒ xiǎng nǐmen de yùnqì yǐjīng jiéshù le." Tā huī le liǎng xià bàng, mǎshàng shā sǐ le liǎng gè qiángdào shǒulǐng. Qítā de qiángdào zhuǎnshēn jiù táo.

Zhège shíhòu, Tángsēng zhèngzài fēikuài de xiàng xī qízhe mǎ, xiàng lìngwài liǎng gè túdì pǎo qù. Tā zǒu dào Zhū hé Shā shēnbiān, chuǎnzhe qì, "Ò, túdìmen, kuài qù nǐmen gēge nàlǐ. Gàosù tā búyào shānghài nàxiē kělián de qiángdào!"

Zhū fēikuài de pǎo xiàng Sūn Wùkōng. Tā zǒu dào hóuzi miànqián shuō,

后取出一根小针，拿在手中。“变！”他小声说。针马上变成了他的金箍棒，十六尺长，像饭碗一样粗。

他把棒放在地上，说，“如果你们中任何人能拿起这根棒，你们就可以留着它。”两个强盗首领想要拿起它，但是就像是苍蝇[7]想要拿起一座山。这是因为这棒重一万三千五百斤[8]。孙悟空拿起棒，说，“现在我想你们的运气已经结束了。”他挥了两下棒，马上杀死了两个强盗首领。其他的强盗转身就逃。

这个时候，唐僧正在飞快地向西骑着马，向另外两个徒弟跑去。他走到猪和沙身边，喘着气，“哦，徒弟们，快去你们哥哥那里。告诉他不要伤害那些可怜的强盗！”

猪飞快地跑向孙悟空。他走到猴子面前说，

---

[7] 苍蝇 cāngyíng – flying

[8] During the Ming Dynasty when this book was written, a cattie was equal to 590 grams, about 1.3 pounds. So the rod weighed almost 9 tons.

"Gēge, shīfu ràng nǐ búyào shā sǐ rènhé qiángdào."

"Wǒ méiyǒu shā sǐ rènhé rén," Sūn Wùkōng dá dào. Tā zhǐzhe dǎo zài dìshàng sǐ le de liǎng gè qiángdào shǒulǐng, shuō, "Tāmen liǎng gè zhǐshì zài shuìjiào."

"Nà hěn qíguài. Tāmen wèishénme shuì zài lù de zhōngjiān? Kěnéng tāmen zhěnggè wǎnshàng dōu bú shuìjiào, zài hējiǔ chànggē." Zhū gèng zǐxì de kàn le kàn. "Tāmen wèishénme zhāngzhe zuǐ shuìjiào?"

"Nà shì yīnwèi wǒ yòng wǒ de bàng dǎ le tāmen. Tāmen yǒngyuǎn bú huì xǐng lái le."

"A, wǒ míngbái le." Zhū huídá dào. Tā pǎo huí Tángsēng shēnbiān, shuō, "Shīfu, hǎo xiāoxi. Qiángdào yǐjīng jiěsàn le."

"Nà hěn hǎo. Tāmen qù nǎlǐ le?"

"Yǒu liǎng gè shénme dìfāng dōu méi qù."

"哥哥，师父让你不要杀死任何强盗。"

"我没有杀死任何人，"孙悟空答道。他指着倒在地上死了的两个强盗首领，说，"他们两个只是在睡觉。"

"那很奇怪。他们为什么睡在路的中间？可能他们整个晚上都不睡觉，在喝酒唱歌。"猪更仔细地看了看。"他们为什么张着嘴睡觉？"

"那是因为我用我的棒打了他们。他们永远不会醒来了。"

"啊，我明白了。"猪回答道。他跑回唐僧身边，说，"师父，好消息。强盗已经解散[9]了。"

"那很好。他们去哪里了？"

"有两个什么地方都没去。"

---

[9] 解散 jiěsàn – to disband

"Nà nǐ wèishénme shuō tāmen jiěsàn le ne?"

"Tāmen bèi dǎ sǐ le. Zhè duì nǐ lái shuō nà búshì jiěsàn le ma?"

Tángsēng tīng le, fēicháng shēngqì. "Zhū, yòng nǐ de bàzi wèi zhè liǎng rén wā fénmù. Ránhòu wǒmen bǎ tāmen mái le. Wǒ yào wèi sǐ le de rén niànjīng." Zhū kāishǐ yòng tā de bàzi wā dòng. Tā wā le sān chǐ zuǒyòu shēn, ránhòu tā de bàzi pèng dào le yìxiē shítou. Tā fàngxià bàzi, yòng tā de bízi hěn kuài de wā wán fénmù. Dāng tā wánchéng shí, dòng yǒu wǔ chǐ shēn. Túdìmen bǎ sǐ le de qiángdào fàng zài dòng lǐ, ránhòu yòng tǔ bǎ tāmen gài zhù. Tángsēng zhàn zài fénmù páng. Tā bǎ shuāngshǒu fàng zài yìqǐ, shuō,

"Xiōngdìmen, wǒ xiàng nǐmen jūgōng, qǐng tīng wǒ shuō
Wǒ láizì dōngfāng, shì Táng huángdì bǎ wǒ sòng lái de
Wǒ zài zhè tiáo lùshàng yùjiàn nǐmen, miànduìmiàn
Nǐmen xiǎng yào wǒ de yīfú hé wǒ de mǎ
Wǒ qiú nǐmen ràng wǒ guòqù, dàn nǐmen bù tīng

“那你为什么说他们解散了呢？”

“他们被打死了。这对你来说那不是解散了吗？”

唐僧听了，非常生气。“猪，用你的耙子为这两人挖[10]坟墓。然后我们把他们埋了。我要为死了的人念经。”猪开始用他的耙子挖洞。他挖了三尺左右深，然后他的耙子碰到了一些石头。他放下耙子，用他的鼻子很快地挖完坟墓。当他完成时，洞有五尺深。徒弟们把死了的强盗放在洞里，然后用土把他们盖住。唐僧站在坟墓旁。他把双手放在一起，说，

“兄弟们，我向你们鞠躬，请听我说
我来自东方，是唐皇帝把我送来的
我在这条路上遇见你们，面对面
你们想要我的衣服和我的马
我求你们让我过去，但你们不听

[10] 挖 wā – to dig

Nǐmen yùjiàn le wǒ de dà túdì, dǎo zài tā de bàng xià
Xiànzài wǒ kělián nǐmen de shītǐ
Rúguǒ nǐmen yùjiàn Yánluó Wáng, qǐng jì zhù
Wǒ de dà túdì xìng Sūn
Wǒ xìng Chén
Wǒ de qítā túdì shì Bājiè hé Wùjìng
Gàosù Yánluó Wáng, shì Sūn shā sǐ le nǐmen, búshì
wǒmen!"

Sūn Wùkōng tīngdào le. Dāng Tángsēng shuō wán, tā shuō, "Shīfu, nǐ zhè jiù bù réncí le ba? Shì de, wǒ shā sǐ le zhèxiē qiángdào. Dàn wǒ zuò zhè dōu shì wèi le nǐ. Zhè shì nǐ de lǚtú, wǒ zhǐshì zài zhèlǐ bāngzhù nǐ. Rúguǒ nǐ méiyǒu juédìng qù xīyóu, zhèxiē rén jiù bú huì sǐ. Rúguǒ nǐ méiyǒu dàizhe wǒ zuò nǐ de túdì, zhèxiē rén jiù bú huì sǐ. Zhè shì nǐ de cuò, búshì wǒ de cuò!" Ránhòu tā zhuǎnxiàng fénmù, shēngqì de shuō,

"Tīng wǒ shuō, nǐmen zhèxiē fēicháng bèn de qiángdào
Nǐmen yícì yòu yícì de dǎ wǒ de tóu
Nǐmen ràng wǒ hěn shēngqì

你们遇见了我的大徒弟，倒在他的棒下
现在我可怜你们的尸体
如果你们遇见阎罗王，请记住
我的大徒弟姓孙
我姓陈
我的其他徒弟是八戒和悟净
告诉阎罗王，是孙杀死了你们，不是我们！”

孙悟空听到了。当唐僧说完，他说，“师父，你这就不仁慈了吧？是的，我杀死了这些强盗。但我做这都是为了你。这是你的旅途，我只是在这里帮助你。如果你没有决定去西游，这些人就不会死。如果你没有带着我做你的徒弟，这些人就不会死。这是你的错，不是我的错！”然后他转向坟墓，生气地说，

“听我说，你们这些非常笨的强盗
你们一次又一次地打我的头
你们让我很生气

Shì de, shā le nǐmen shì ge cuòwù

Dàn wǒ búpà nǐmen

Wǒ búpà Yánluó Wáng

Wǒ shì Qí Tiān Dàshèng

Dìyù lǐ de shí gè dàwáng dōu wèi wǒ gōngzuò

Yùhuángdàdì rèndé wǒ

Tàishān de shǒuwèi pà wǒ

Tiānshàng de zhòng shén dōu shì

Wǒ de péngyǒu nǐmen kěyǐ qù dìyù gào wǒ

Wǒ búzàihū!"

Tángsēng tīng le zhè huà. Tā hěn chījīng Sūn Wùkōng huì zhème shēngqì. "Túdì, wǒ de huà shì wèi le ràng nǐ kàn dào shēngmìng de jiàzhí, ràng nǐ chéngwéi gèng hǎo de rén. Nǐ wèishénme zhème bù gāoxìng?"

"Shīfu," Sūn Wùkōng shuō, "nǐ de huà búshì zài kāiwánxiào." Tā kāishǐ wǎng xī zǒu, ránhòu zhuǎnshēn yòu shuō, "Ràng wǒmen zhǎo jīntiān wǎnshàng zhù de dìfāng." Tángsēng hé lìngwài liǎng gè tú

是的，杀了你们是个错误[11]

但我不怕你们

我不怕阎罗王

我是齐天大圣

地狱里的十个大王都为我工作

玉皇大帝认得我

泰山的守卫怕我

天上的众神都是我的朋友

你们可以去地狱告我

我不在乎！”

唐僧听了这话。他很吃惊孙悟空会这么生气。“徒弟，我的话是为了让你看到生命的价值[12]，让你成为更好的人。你为什么这么不高兴？”

“师父，”孙悟空说，“你的话不是在开玩笑。”他开始往西走，然后转身又说，“让我们找今天晚上住的地方。”唐僧和另外两个徒

---

[11] 错误 cuòwù – mistake
[12] 价值 jiàzhí – value

dì gēn zài tā shēnhòu. Sì gè rén dōu bù gāoxìng, yǒuxiē shēngqì. Kōngqì zhōng mǎn shì jǐnzhāng de qìfēn.

Hěn kuài, tāmen lái dào le yígè xiǎo cūnzhuāng. Kàn le sìzhōu, tāmen fāxiàn zhè shì yígè búcuò de dìfāng. Tāmen tīngdào gǒu jiào shēng, kàndào xiǎo wūzi chuānghù shàng diǎnzhe de làzhú. Yí wèi lǎorén cóng yì jiān xiǎo wūzi lǐ zǒu le chūlái. Tángsēng xiàng tā wènhǎo. "Nǐ hǎo, yéye. Wǒmen qiánwǎng xītiān, zhǎo fó de shèng shū. Yǐjīng hěn wǎn le, wǒmen xiǎng zhǎo ge dìfāng guòyè. Qǐng búyào pà wǒ de túdì. Tāmen hěn chǒu, dàn tāmen bú huì shānghài nǐ."

Lǎorén kànzhe túdì. Tā shuō, "Tāmen fēicháng chǒu. Yígè kàn shàngqù xiàng yèchā, yígè shì mǎ liǎn, yígè shì léishén."

Sūn Wùkōng hái zài shēngqì. Tā huídá shuō, "Lǎorén, léishén shì wǒ de sūnzi, yèchā shì wǒ érzi de sūnzi, mǎ liǎn shì wǒ sūnzi de sūnzi." Lǎorén tīng le, xià huài le. Tā liǎn biàn bái, dǎo zài dìshàng. Tángsēng bāngzhe tā zhàn qǐlái, shuō, "Bié dān

弟跟在他身后。四个人都不高兴，有些生气。空气中满是紧张的气氛[13]。

很快，他们来到了一个小村庄。看了四周，他们发现这是一个不错的地方。他们听到狗叫声，看到小屋子窗户上点着的蜡烛。一位老人从一间小屋子里走了出来。唐僧向他问好。"你好，爷爷。我们前往西天，找佛的圣书。已经很晚了，我们想找个地方过夜。请不要怕我的徒弟。他们很丑，但他们不会伤害你。"

老人看着徒弟。他说，"他们非常丑。一个看上去像夜叉[14]，一个是马脸，一个是雷神。"

孙悟空还在生气。他回答说，"老人，雷神是我的孙子[15]，夜叉是我儿子的孙子，马脸是我孙子的孙子。"老人听了，吓坏了。他脸变白，倒在地上。唐僧帮着他站起来，说，"别担

---

[13] 气氛　qìfēn – atmosphere
[14] 夜叉　yèchā – yaksa, a troublemaking nature spirit
[15] 孙子　sūnzi – grandson

xīn, wǒ de péngyǒu, tāmen dōu hěn cūlǔ, bù zhīdào zěnme lǐmào de shuōhuà. Nǐ jiào léishén de nàge rén, shì wǒ de dà túdì Sūn Wùkōng. Nǐ jiào mǎ liǎn de nàge rén, shì wǒ de dì èr ge túdì Zhū Bājiè. Nǐ jiào yèchā de nàge rén, shì wǒ de dì sān ge túdì Shā Wùjìng. Tāmen búshì móguǐ. Bié hàipà."

"Hǎo le, jìnlái ba," Lǎorén shuō. Tāmen jìn le tā de wūzi. Lǎorén ràng tā de qīzi qù bǎ chá ná lái. Tā qù chúfáng pào chá. Yígè xiǎo nánhái gēnzhe tā.

"Yéye," Tángsēng shuō, "nǐ xìng shénme, jǐ suì le?"

"Wǒ xìng Yáng. Wǒ yǐjīng huó le qīshísì nián le. Wǒ yǒu yígè érzi. Nǐ zài zhèlǐ kàn dào de xiǎo háizi shì wǒ de sūnzi."

"Wǒ xiǎng jiàn jiàn nǐ érzi." Tángsēng shuō.

"Nà niánqīng rén búpèi jiàn nǐ zhèyàng de shèng sēng. Wǒ xīwàng tā yǒu yí fèn hǎo gōngzuò. Dàn tā zhǐ xiǎng shārén, ná zǒu tāmen de qián. Tā de péngyǒu dōu shì huàirén. Tā wǔ tiān qián chūqù le, hái méiyǒu

心，我的朋友，他们都很粗鲁，不知道怎么礼貌[16]地说话。你叫雷神的那个人，是我的大徒弟孙悟空。你叫马脸的那个人，是我的第二个徒弟猪八戒。你叫夜叉的那个人，是我的第三个徒弟沙悟净。他们不是魔鬼。别害怕。”

“好了，进来吧，”老人说。他们进了他的屋子。老人让他的妻子去把茶拿来。她去厨房泡茶。一个小男孩跟着她。

“爷爷，”唐僧说，“你姓什么，几岁了？”

“我姓杨。我已经活了七十四年了。我有一个儿子。你在这里看到的小孩子是我的孙子。”

“我想见见你儿子。”唐僧说。

“那年轻人不配[17]见你这样的圣僧。我希望他有一份好工作。但他只想杀人，拿走他们的钱。他的朋友都是坏人。他五天前出去了，还没有

---

16 礼貌 lǐmào – polite
17 不配 búpèi – unworthy

huílái."

Tángsēng xiǎngzhe zhè. Tā xiǎng zhīdào Sūn Wùkōng shì búshì nàtiān zǎo xiē shíhòu zài lùshàng shā le tāmen de érzi. Tā hái méi shuōhuà, Sūn Wùkōng jiù duì lǎorén shuō, "Xiānshēng, zhème huài de érzi, zhǐ huì gěi nǐ hé nǐ de jiārén dài lái máfan. Wèishénme yào liú tā? Ràng wǒ qù zhǎo tā. Wǒ kěyǐ bāng nǐ shā le tā!"

"Wǒ kěnéng huì ràng nǐ nàyàng zuò, dànshì wǒ méiyǒu qítā de érzi. Wǒ érzi biàn chéng le huàirén, zhè shì zhēn de, dàn wǒ sǐ hòu xūyào yǒurén bāng wǒ wā fénmù."

Sūn Wùkōng hái méiyǒu huídá, Shā mǎshàng jiù shuō, "Gēge, zuò hǎo nǐ zìjǐ de shì ba." Tā zhuǎnxiàng lǎorén shuō, "Yéye, nǐ hé nǐ de jiārén duì wǒmen hěn hǎo. Qǐng gàosù wǒmen, jīntiān wǎnshàng wǒmen kěyǐ zài nǎlǐ shuìjiào." Lǎorén dài tāmen dào le gǔ cāng. Tā bǎ yìxiē gānjìng de cǎo fàng zài dìshàng, gěi yóurénmen shuìjiào. Hěn kuài, sì gè rén dōu shuìzháo le.

Xiànzài, Yáng de érzi zhēn de shì qiángdào zhōng de yígè, dàn tā bú

回来。”

唐僧想着这。他想知道孙悟空是不是那天早些时候在路上杀了他们的儿子。他还没说话，孙悟空就对老人说，“先生，这么坏的儿子，只会给你和你的家人带来麻烦。为什么要留他？让我去找他。我可以帮你杀了他！”

“我可能会让你那样做，但是我没有其他的儿子。我儿子变成了坏人，这是真的，但我死后需要有人帮我挖坟墓。”

孙悟空还没有回答，沙马上就说，“哥哥，做好你自己的事吧。”他转向老人说，“爷爷，你和你的家人对我们很好。请告诉我们，今天晚上我们可以在哪里睡觉。”老人带他们到了谷仓[18]。他把一些干净的草放在地上，给游人们睡觉。很快，四个人都睡着了。

现在，杨的儿子真的是强盗中的一个，但他不

[18] 谷仓　　gǔ cāng – barn

shì qiángdào shǒulǐng zhōng de yígè. Nàtiān zǎo xiē shíhòu, Sūn Wùkōng shā sǐ le qiángdào shǒulǐng hòu, Yáng de érzi hé qítā qiángdào táopǎo le. Nàtiān wǎnshàng, yóurénmen shàngchuáng shuìjiào hòu, qiángdào qiāo le Yáng jiā de mén. Lǎorén kāi le mén. Qiángdào pǎo jìn wū lǐ, hǎn dào, "Wǒmen è le!" Yáng de érzi de qīzi xǐng le. Tā kāishǐ wèi qiángdàomen zhǔ fàn. Yáng de érzi dào wū hòu qù ná shāohuǒ de mùtou. Tā kàndào le Tángsēng de báimǎ. Tā huí dào wū lǐ, wèn tā de bàba, "Wū hòu nà pǐ báimǎ shì shénme?"

Lǎorén huídá shuō, "zhè pǐ mǎ shì lǚyóu sēngrén de. Tāmen yào qù xītiān. Tāmen xiǎng jīntiān wǎnshàng tāmen kěyǐ shuì zài zhèlǐ."

Yáng de érzi pāi le pāi shǒu, duì tā de péngyǒumen shuō, "Hǎo xiāoxi, péngyǒumen! Wǒmen de dírén zài zhèlǐ! Wǒmen jīntiān wǎnshàng kěyǐ shā sǐ tāmen. Wǒmen kěyǐ ná zǒu tāmen de mǎ hé tāmen de qián."

Yígè qiángdào shuō, "Ràng wǒmen děng yíxià. Ràng wǒmen xiān chī diǎn

是强盗首领中的一个。那天早些时候，孙悟空杀死了强盗首领后，杨的儿子和其他强盗逃跑了。那天晚上，游人们上床睡觉后，强盗敲了杨家的门。老人开了门。强盗跑进屋里，喊道，“我们饿了！”杨的儿子的妻子醒了。她开始为强盗们煮饭。杨的儿子到屋后去拿烧火的木头。他看到了唐僧的白马。他回到屋里，问他的爸爸，“屋后那匹白马是什么？”

老人回答说，“这匹马是旅游僧人的。他们要去西天。他们想今天晚上他们可以睡在这里。”

杨的儿子拍了拍手，对他的朋友们说，“好消息，朋友们！我们的敌人[19]在这里！我们今天晚上可以杀死他们。我们可以拿走他们的马和他们的钱。”

一个强盗说，“让我们等一下。让我们先吃点

---

[19] 敌人　　dírén – enemy

wǎnfàn, mó yíxià wǒmen de dāo. Jīntiān wǎnshàng wǎn xiē shíhòu, wǒmen kěyǐ shā sǐ tāmen." Suǒyǐ tāmen dōu zuò xiàlái chī wǎnfàn, mó dāo.

Zài tāmen chī wǎnfàn de shíhòu, lǎorén qiāoqiāo de zǒujìn le gǔ cāng. Tā jiào xǐng yóurén, gàosù tāmen qiángdào zhèng dǎsuàn shā sǐ tāmen. "Kuài pǎo!" tā shuō. Yóurénmen ná qǐ tāmen de xínglǐ, líkāi le gǔ cāng, zǒu shàng xiàng xī de lù.

Zài wǔ gēng zuǒyòu de shíhòu, qiángdàomen juédìng gōngjī de shíhòu dào le. Tāmen pǎo chū fángzi, pǎo jìn gǔ cāng. Dànshì dāngrán, yóurénmen yǐjīng zǒu le. Qiángdào dàizhe dāo hé máo kāishǐ zài lùshàng xiàng xī pǎo. Hěn kuài, tāmen jiù zhuī shàng le yóurén.

Sūn Wùkōng tíng xià, zhuǎnshēn duìzhe qiángdào. "Túdì," Tángsēng shuō, "nǐ bù kěyǐ shānghài zhèxiē rén. Zhǐshì xià xià tāmen, ràng tāmen zǒu kāi."

Sūn Wùkōng bù lǐ tā. Qiángdào bǎ Sūn Wùkōng wéi zài zhōngjiān. Tāmen kāishǐ yòng dāo hé máo gōngjī tā. Hóu wáng kāishǐ huīdòng tā de Jīn Gū Bàng, yuè lái yuè kuài. Dāng tā jī zhòng qiángdào shí, tāmen xiàng xīngxing

晚饭，磨一下我们的刀。今天晚上晚些时候，我们可以杀死他们。”所以他们都坐下来吃晚饭，磨刀。

在他们吃晚饭的时候，老人悄悄地走进了谷仓。他叫醒游人，告诉他们强盗正打算杀死他们。“快跑！”他说。游人们拿起他们的行李，离开了谷仓，走上向西的路。

在五更左右的时候，强盗们决定攻击的时候到了。他们跑出房子，跑进谷仓。但是当然，游人们已经走了。强盗带着刀和矛开始在路上向西跑。很快，他们就追上了游人。

孙悟空停下，转身对着强盗。“徒弟，”唐僧说，“你不可以伤害这些人。只是吓吓他们，让他们走开。”

孙悟空不理他。强盗把孙悟空围在中间。他们开始用刀和矛攻击他。猴王开始挥动他的金箍棒，越来越快。当他击中强盗时，他们像星星

yíyàng dǎo xià. Yǒu jǐ gè rén táozǒu le, yǒu jǐ gè rén shòu le shāng, dàn dà duōshù rén dōu bèi shā sǐ le. Tāmen de shītǐ tǎng zài dìshàng.

Tángsēng hěn bù gāoxìng. Tā qímǎ líkāi le zhàndòu. Sūn Wùkōng pǎo dào yì míng shòushāng de qiángdào shēnbiān, shuō, “Yáng de érzi zài nǎlǐ?” Qiángdào zhǐzhe yígè rén shuō, “Zài nàlǐ, nàge chuān huángsè yīfú de rén.” Sūn Wùkōng pǎo dào nàge chuān huángsè yīfú rén miànqián, kǎn xià le tā de tóu. Bǎ tā ná qǐlái, tā pǎo dào Tángsēng miànqián shuō, “Shīfu, zhè shì Yáng lǎorén de érzi. Wǒ yǐjīng kǎn diào le tā de tóu.”

Tángsēng dǎo zài dìshàng, jiào dào, “Bǎ tā ná kāi! Bǎ tā ná kāi!” Zhū bǎ tóu tī dào lù biān. Ránhòu tā yòng bàzi wā le yígè xiǎo dòng, bǎ tóu mái le.

Shā zǒu dào Tángsēng shēnbiān, bāng tā zhàn le qǐlái. Tángsēng kāishǐ niàn jǐn tóu dài mó yǔ. Sūn Wùkōng tóu shàng de tóu dài mǎshàng biàn dé gèng jǐn le. Sūn Wùkōng tòngkǔ de jiàozhe. Tángsēng yícì yòu yícì de niàn

一样倒下。有几个人逃走了，有几个人受了伤，但大多数[20]人都被杀死了。他们的尸体躺在地上。

唐僧很不高兴。他骑马离开了战斗。孙悟空跑到一名受伤的强盗身边，说，“杨的儿子在哪里？”强盗指着一个人说，“在那里，那个穿黄色衣服的人。”孙悟空跑到那个穿黄色衣服人面前，砍下了他的头。把它拿起来，他跑到唐僧面前说，“师父，这是杨老人的儿子。我已经砍掉了他的头。”

唐僧倒在地上，叫道，“把它拿开！把它拿开！”猪把头踢到路边。然后他用耙子挖了一个小洞，把头埋了。

沙走到唐僧身边，帮他站了起来。唐僧开始念紧头带魔语。孙悟空头上的头带马上变得更紧了。孙悟空痛苦的叫着。唐僧一次又一次地念

[20] 大多数 dà duōshù – most of

zhe jǐn tóu dài mó yǔ. Tā niàn le shí cì. Tóu dài jǐn le shí bèi. Sūn Wùkōng tǎng zài dìshàng, shuāngshǒu fàng zài tóu shàng, tòng dé dà jiào, shuō, "Shīfu, qiú nǐ tíng xiàlái!"

Tángsēng duì tā shuō, "Wǒ méiyǒu huà kěyǐ hé nǐ shuō. Wǒ bú zài xiǎng yào nǐ zuò wǒ de túdì le. Yáng de érzi shì bù hǎo, dàn tā yě bù yīng gāi bèi nǐ shā sǐ. Nǐ shā le tài duō de rén, zhǎo le tài duō de máfan. Nǐ méiyǒu réncí. Zǒu ba, bié huílái le!"

Sūn Wùkōng shuāngshǒu bào tóu jiào dào, "Tíngzhǐ niànjīng!" Ránhòu tā yòng tā de jīndǒu yún, xiāoshī bújiàn le.

着紧头带魔语。他念了十次。头带紧了十倍。孙悟空躺在地上，双手放在头上，痛得大叫，说，“师父，求你停下来！”

唐僧对他说，“我没有话可以和你说。我不再想要你做我的徒弟了。杨的儿子是不好，但他也不应该被你杀死。你杀了太多的人，找了太多的麻烦。你没有仁慈。走吧，别回来了！”

孙悟空双手抱头叫道，“停止念经！”然后他用他的筋斗云，消失不见了。

Dì 57 Zhāng

Sūn Wùkōng zhǐ néng líkāi, dànshì tā kěyǐ qù nǎlǐ ne? Tā xiǎng huí Huāguǒ Shān de jiā, dàn tā pà yīnwèi tā méiyǒu gēnzhe tā de shīfu, qítā hóuzi qiáobùqǐ tā. Tā xiǎng qù tiāngōng, dàn tā pà tiānshén bú ràng tā liú zài nàlǐ. Tā xiǎng hé tā de péngyǒu Dōng Hǎi Lóngwáng zhù zài yìqǐ, dàn tā bùxiǎng yīnwèi tā shì yígè méiyǒu jiā kěyǐ huí de hóuzi cái qù nàlǐ. Zuìhòu tā háishì juédìng huí dào Tángsēng nàlǐ, xiàng tā shuō duìbùqǐ.

Tā yòng tā de jīndǒu yún, lái dào Tángsēng de mǎ qián, shuō, "Shīfu, qǐng yuánliàng wǒ. Wǒ bú huì zài shānghài huò shā sǐ biérén le. Wǒ qiú nǐ, ràng wǒ hé nǐ yìqǐ qù xītiān."

Dànshì Tángsēng háishì duì Sūn Wùkōng hěn shēngqì. Tā zhǐshì yòu kāishǐ yí cì cì de niàn jǐn tóu dài mó yǔ, niàn le èrshí cì. Xiànzài de tóu dài biàn dé fēicháng de jǐn, jìnrù le Sūn Wùkōng de ròu lǐ, yǒu yícùn shēn. Tángsēng shuō, "Nǐ zěnme yòu lái wǒ zhèlǐ zhǎo má

第 57 章

孙悟空只能离开，但是他可以去哪里呢？他想回花果山的家，但他怕因为他没有跟着他的师父，其他猴子瞧不起[21]他。他想去天宫，但他怕天神不让他留在那里。他想和他的朋友东海龙王住在一起，但他不想因为他是一个没有家可以回的猴子才去那里。最后他还是决定回到唐僧那里，向他说对不起。

他用他的筋斗云，来到唐僧的马前，说，“师父，请原谅我。我不会再伤害或杀死别人了。我求你，让我和你一起去西天。”

但是唐僧还是对孙悟空很生气。他只是又开始一次次地念紧头带魔语，念了二十次。现在的头带变得非常的紧，进入了孙悟空的肉里，有一寸深。唐僧说，“你怎么又来我这里找麻

[21] 瞧不起 qiáobùqǐ – to look down

fan? Kuài líkāi."

"Shīfu, nǐ xūyào wǒ de bāngzhù. Rúguǒ méiyǒu wǒ, wǒ xiǎng nǐ zǒu bú dào xītiān."

Tángsēng huídá shuō, "Nǐ shì shārén húsūn. Wǒ búyào nǐ le. Kěnéng wǒ huì zǒu dào xītiān, kěnéng wǒ bú huì, dàn zhè hé nǐ méiguānxì. Xiànzài líkāi. Rúguǒ nǐ bù líkāi, wǒ huì jìxù niàn jǐn tóu dài mó yǔ, zhídào nǐ sǐ."

Sūn Wùkōng shāngxīn de zàicì shàng dào yún zhōng. Tā juédìng qù Pǔtuóluòjiā Shān jiàn Guānyīn púsà.

Yígè xiǎoshí hòu, tā lái dào le nán dàhǎi. Tā fēi dào le Pǔtuóluòjiā Shān, ránhòu jìnrù le Guānyīn de zǐzhú lín. Guānyīn túdì Mùchā jiàn le tā, shuō, "Dà shèng wèishénme lái zhèlǐ?"

"Wǒ yǒu huà yào gàosù púsà."

Mùchā xiǎng wèn tā yìxiē wèntí, dàn jiù zài zhè shí, yì zhī měilì de bái niǎo chūxiàn le. Tā láilái huíhuí de fēizhe. Zhè jiùshì shuō Guānyīn yǐjīng zhǔnbèi hǎo jiàn tā le. Sūn Wùkōng zǒu jìn Guānyīn. Tā

烦？快离开。”

“师父，你需要我的帮助。如果没有我，我想你走不到西天。”

唐僧回答说，“你是杀人猢狲。我不要你了。可能我会走到西天，可能我不会，但这和你没关系。现在离开。如果你不离开，我会继续念紧头带魔语，直到你死。”

孙悟空伤心的再次上到云中。他决定去普陀洛迦山见观音菩萨。

一个小时后，他来到了南大海。他飞到了普陀洛迦山，然后进入了观音的紫竹林。观音徒弟木叉见了他，说，“大圣为什么来这里？”

“我有话要告诉菩萨。”

木叉想问他一些问题，但就在这时，一只美丽的白鸟出现了。它来来回回地飞着。这就是说观音已经准备好见他了。孙悟空走近观音。他

kāishǐ kū le. Guānyīn shuō, "Wùkōng, gàosù wǒ nǐ wèishénme kū. Wǒ huì bāng nǐ."

"Nǐ bǎ wǒ cóng jiānyù lǐ fàng le chūlái, ràng wǒ zǒu shàng fó de dàolù. Cóng nàge shíhòu kāishǐ, wǒ jiù yìzhí gēnzhe Tángsēng, bǎohù tā bú shòudào yāoguài, móguǐ hé huāngyě lǐ de dòngwù de shānghài. Wǒ zěnme zhīdào tā huì zhème bù gǎnxiè wǒ? Zhēn de, tā bù zhīdào shénme shì hēi, shénme shì bái."

Guānyīn xiàozhe shuō, "Wùkōng, gàosù wǒ gèng duō hēi hé bái de shì."

Sūn Wùkōng bǎ yíqiè dōu gàosù le tā. Tā gàosù tā guānyú qiángdào de shì. Tā gàosù tā Tángsēng shì zěnme yòng jǐn tóu dài mó yǔ de. Tā gàosù tā, xiànzài tiānshàng rénjiān dōu méiyǒu tā kěyǐ qù de dìfāng.

Guānyīn tīng le. Shuō, "Tángsēng shì shèng sēng, tā bú huì shārén, yígè dōu bù huì shā. Dànshì nǐ shā le hěnduō rén. Shā móguǐ huò yāoguài kěyǐ, dàn nǐ bùnéng shārén. Nǐ kěyǐ hěn róngyì de xià pǎo nàxiē rén, búshì qù shā sǐ tāmen. Zài wǒ kàn, nǐ zuò

开始哭了。观音说，“悟空，告诉我你为什么哭。我会帮你。”

“你把我从监狱里放了出来，让我走上佛的道路。从那个时候开始，我就一直跟着唐僧，保护他不受到妖怪、魔鬼和荒野里的动物的伤害。我怎么知道他会这么不感谢我？真的，他不知道什么是黑，什么是白。”

观音笑着说，“悟空，告诉我更多黑和白的事。”

孙悟空把一切都告诉了她。他告诉她关于强盗的事。他告诉她唐僧是怎么用紧头带魔语的。他告诉她，现在天上人间都没有他可以去的地方。

观音听了。说，“唐僧是圣僧，他不会杀人，一个都不会杀。但是你杀了很多人。杀魔鬼或妖怪可以，但你不能杀人。你可以很容易地吓跑那些人，不是去杀死他们。在我看，你做

dé hěn bù hǎo."

"Wǒ míngbái. Dàn wǒ bù yīng gāi bèi zhèyàng duìdài. Wǒ qiú qiú nǐ, qǐng gěi wǒ yìxiē réncí. Qǐng bǎ wǒ cóng zhège shénqí de tóu dài zhōng fàng chūlái. Ràng wǒ huí Huāguǒ Shān, ānjìng de zhù zài nàlǐ."

"Wǒ hěn duìbùqǐ, dàn wǒ bùnéng nàyàng zuò. Fózǔ tā zìjǐ gěi le wǒ zhège tóu dài fàng zài nǐ tóu shàng. Tā hái jiāo le wǒ jǐn tóu dài mó yǔ. Dàn pà shì méiyǒu sōng tóu dài mó yǔ."

"Nà hǎo ba. Wǒ xièxiè nǐ. Wǒ xiànzài jiù zǒu."

"Nǐ yào qù nǎlǐ?"

"Wǒ qù jiàn fózǔ, qǐng tā bǎ tóu dài cóng wǒ de tóu shàng ná zǒu." Tā zhàn qǐlái, zhǔnbèi líkāi.

"Bù, děng děng. Wǒ xiǎng wèi nǐ kàn kàn wèilái."

"Qǐng búyào nàyàng. Wǒ bùxiǎng kàndào wǒ de wèilái."

得很不好。”

“我明白。但我不应该被这样对待[22]。我求求你，请给我一些仁慈。请把我从这个神奇的头带中放出来。让我回花果山，安静地住在那里。”

“我很对不起，但我不能那样做。佛祖他自己给了我这个头带放在你头上。他还教了我紧头带魔语。但怕是没有松头带魔语。”

“那好吧。我谢谢你。我现在就走。”

“你要去哪里？”

“我去见佛祖，请他把头带从我的头上拿走。”他站起来，准备离开。

“不，等等。我想为你看看未来。”

“请不要那样。我不想看到我的未来。”

[22] 对待 duìdài – to treat

"Búshì nǐ de wèilái. Shì Tángsēng de wèilái." Tā bì shàng le tā de yǎnjīng, kàn xiàng le sān gè shìjiè. Tā zhāng kāi le yǎnjīng, shuō, "Wùkōng, nǐ shīfu kěnéng hěn kuài huì sǐ. Tā huì xūyào nǐ. Wǒ huì ràng tā bǎ nǐ dài huíqù, zhèyàng nǐmen liǎ kěyǐ zǒu dào nǐmen lǚtú de zuìhòu, dédào zhìhuì." Sūn Wùkōng bù gǎn shuō shénme.

Jiù zài Sūn Wùkōng jiàn Guānyīn de shíhòu, Tángsēng hé tā de lìngwài liǎng gè túdì jìxù tāmen de lǚtú. Jiējìn wǎnshàng de shíhòu, Tángsēng yǐjīng fēicháng è le. Tā ràng Zhū zài fùjìn zhǎo ge cūnzi, tā kěyǐ yào yìxiē mǐfàn. Zhū kàn le, dàn méiyǒu kàndào fùjìn yǒu cūnzhuāng. Tángsēng shuō, "Nà nǐ gěi wǒ ná diǎn hé shuǐ. Wǒ fēicháng kě." Zhū líkāi qù ná shuǐ.

Tángsēng hé Shā děng le hěnjiǔ, dàn Zhū méiyǒu huílái. Zuìhòu, Shā líkāi qù ná shuǐ. Tángsēng zhège shíhòu yígè rén, zuò zài lù biān. Tā tīng dào yígè hěn xiǎng de shēngyīn, táitóu kàn. Sūn Wùkōng názhe yì wǎn shuǐ zhàn zài tā miànqián, shuō, "Shīfu, wǒ huílái le. Zhè lǐ yǒu yìxiē shuǐ. Hē ba!"

Dànshì Tángsēng háishì hěn shēngqì. Tā shuō, "Wǒ búyào nǐ de

“不是你的未来。是唐僧的未来。”她闭上了她的眼睛，看向了三个世界。她张开了眼睛，说，“悟空，你师父可能很快会死。他会需要你。我会让他把你带回去，这样你们俩可以走到你们旅途的最后，得到智慧。”孙悟空不敢说什么。

就在孙悟空见观音的时候，唐僧和他的另外两个徒弟继续他们的旅途。接近晚上的时候，唐僧已经非常饿了。他让猪在附近找个村子，他可以要一些米饭。猪看了，但没有看到附近有村庄。唐僧说，“那你给我拿点河水。我非常渴。”猪离开去拿水。

唐僧和沙等了很久，但猪没有回来。最后，沙离开去拿水。唐僧这个时候一个人，坐在路边。他听到一个很响的声音，抬头看。孙悟空拿着一碗水站在他面前，说，“师父，我回来了。这里有一些水。喝吧！”

但是唐僧还是很生气。他说，“我不要你的

shuǐ, wǒ yě búyào nǐ. Duì wǒ lái shuō, kě sǐ bǐ ràng nǐ huílái hǎo. Xiànzài líkāi zhèlǐ!" Sūn Wùkōng shēngqì le. Tā bǎ Tángsēng dǎdǎo zài dìshàng. Ránhòu tā zhuā qǐ xínglǐ, yòng tā de jīndǒu yún fēi zǒu le.

Zhū zhèng zhǔnbèi qù hé lǐ qǔshuǐ, dàn tā táitóu kàn, kàn dào yì jiān xiǎo péng wū. Tā juédìng qù nàlǐ yào shíwù. Tā bùxiǎng ràng zìjǐ de yàngzi xiàdào rén, suǒyǐ tā niàn le yígè mó yǔ, shēntǐ yáo le jǐ xià. Tā biàn chéng le yígè huáng pífū, yòu bìng yòu lǎo de héshang.

"Bāng bang máng, bāng bang máng," tā duìzhe fángzi de mén shuō, "Wǒ shì ge qióng héshang. Qǐng gěi wǒ yìxiē mǐfàn!" Wū lǐ yǒu liǎng gè nǚrén. Tāmen pà shēngbìng de héshang, suǒyǐ tāmen mǎshàng bǎ tā yàofàn de wǎn zhuāng mǎn le fàn, gěi le tā.

Zhū názhe mǐfàn huílái de shíhòu, zài lùshàng yù dào le Shā. Zhū yòng tā de cháng yī jiē zhù cóng yàofàn de wǎn lǐ dào chūlái de mǐfàn, ránhòu tāmen yòng yàofàn de wǎn zhuāng mǎn le hé lǐ de shuǐ. Ránhòu tāmen jiù huí dào le tāmen líkāi Tángsēng de dìfāng. Kěshì dāng tāmen dào le nàge dìfāng de shíhòu, kàndào Tángsēng de liǎn xiàng xià dǎo zài

水，我也不要你。对我来说，渴死比让你回来好。现在离开这里！”孙悟空生气了。他把唐僧打倒在地上。然后他抓起行李，用他的筋斗云飞走了。

猪正准备去河里取水，但他抬头看，看到一间小棚屋。他决定去那里要食物。他不想让自己的样子吓到人，所以他念了一个魔语，身体摇了几下。他变成了一个黄皮肤、又病又老的和尚。

“帮帮忙，帮帮忙，”他对着房子的门说，“我是个穷和尚。请给我一些米饭！”屋里有两个女人。他们怕生病的和尚，所以她们马上把他要饭的碗装满了饭，给了他。

猪拿着米饭回来的时候，在路上遇到了沙。猪用他的长衣接住从要饭的碗里倒出来的米饭，然后他们用要饭的碗装满了河里的水。然后他们就回到了他们离开唐僧的地方。可是当他们到了那个地方的时候，看到唐僧的脸向下倒在

dìshàng. Tā kàn qǐlái xiàng sǐ le yíyàng. Xínglǐ bújiàn le.

"Wánle, wánle!" Zhū jiào dào. "Wǒmen jiéshù le. Búyào zàishuō qù xītiān qǔjīng le. Nǐ liú zài zhèlǐ, kànzhe shīfu de shītǐ. Wǒ qù xià yígè chéngshì, mǎi yìkǒu guāncai, zhèyàng wǒmen jiù kěyǐ bǎ tā mái le. Zhè yǐhòu, wǒmen liǎ dōu kěyǐ huí jiā, wàngjì zhège lǚtú."

Shā bǎ Tángsēng de shēntǐ fān guòlái, tā wān xià yāo, zǐxì kàn. Tā kàndào Tángsēng qīng qīng de hūxīzhe. "Shīfu hái huózhe!" Shā shuō.

Tāmen děngzhe, zhídào Tángsēng yòu hūxī le jǐ cì, zhāng kāi le tā de yǎnjīng. Tā duì túdìmen shuō, "Shì nàge wúfǎwútiān de hóuzi. Nǐmen zǒu hòu bùjiǔ, hóuzi huílái le. Wǒ jiào tā zǒu kāi. Tā dǎ le wǒ, yǐwéi wǒ sǐ le, jiù líkāi le."

Tāmen huí dào le Zhū nàtiān zǎo xiē shíhòu yàofàn de nà jiān xiǎo péng wū. Liǎng gè nǚrén zhōng de yígè dǎkāi mén shuō, "Shénme, gèng duō de héshang? Jīntiān zǎo xiē shíhòu wǒ kàndào yígè yòu lǎo yòu bìng

地上。他看起来像死了一样。行李不见了。

“完了，完了！”猪叫道。“我们结束了。不要再说去西天取经了。你留在这里，看着师父的尸体。我去下一个城市，买一口棺材，这样我们就可以把他埋了。这以后，我们俩都可以回家，忘记这个旅途。”

沙把唐僧的身体翻过来，他弯下腰[23]，仔细看。他看到唐僧轻轻地呼吸着。“师父还活着！”沙说。

他们等着，直到唐僧又呼吸了几次，张开了他的眼睛。他对徒弟们说，“是那个无法无天的猴子。你们走后不久，猴子回来了。我叫他走开。他打了我，以为我死了，就离开了。”

他们回到了猪那天早些时候要饭的那间小棚屋。两个女人中的一个打开门说，“什么，更多的和尚？今天早些时候我看到一个又老又病

---

[23] 弯下腰 wān xiàyāo – to bend over (“bend down waist”)

de héshang, gěi le tā yìxiē mǐfàn. Wǒ méiyǒu shénme kěyǐ gěi nǐmen le. Qǐng nǐmen zǒu kāi, bié lái gěi wǒ zhǎo máfan."

Zhū gàosù nà nǚrén, tā jiùshì tā jiànguò de shēngbìng de héshang. Ránhòu Tángsēng jiěshì shuō tāmen zhèng qù xītiān, tā de dà túdì dǎ le tā de tóu, ránhòu táopǎo le. Tā wèn tāmen shì búshì kěyǐ zài tā jiā xiūxi. Tā tóngyì le, gěi tāmen yìxiē rè chá hē. Tángsēng hē le chá. Guò le yīhuǐ'er, tā gǎnjué hǎoduō le. Tā duì tā de túdì shuō, "Nǐmen zhōng de yígè yídìng yào qù zhǎo nàge wúfǎwútiān de hóuzi. Tā nà lǐ yǒu wǒmen de xínglǐ, lǐmiàn yǒu wǒmen de tōngguān wénshū. Nǐmen bìxū bǎ wǒmen de xínglǐ dài huílái, zhèyàng wǒmen cáinéng jìxù wǒmen de lǚtú."

"Wǒ qù," Zhū huídá shuō. "Wǒ yǐqián qùguò Huāguǒ Shān. Wǒ rènshí lù."

"Bù," Tángsēng huídá. "Nà zhī hóuzi bù xǐhuān nǐ. Nǐ shuō de huà chángcháng hěn cūlǔ. Tā kěnéng huì hěn shēngqì, huì gōngjī nǐ." Ránhòu tā zhuǎnxiàng Shā Wùjìng shuō, "Shā, nǐ bìxū qù. Zhǎodào nàge hóuzi. Rúguǒ tā yuànyì bǎ xínglǐ gěi nǐ, jiù názhe, ránhòu huí dào zhèlǐ. Rúguǒ tā jùjué, búyào hé

的和尚，给了他一些米饭。我没有什么可以给你们了。请你们走开，别来给我找麻烦。”

猪告诉那女人，他就是她见过的生病的和尚。然后唐僧解释说他们正去西天，他的大徒弟打了他的头，然后逃跑了。他问他们是不是可以在她家休息。她同意了，给他们一些热茶喝。唐僧喝了茶。过了一会儿，他感觉好多了。他对他的徒弟说，“你们中的一个一定要去找那个无法无天的猴子。他那里有我们的行李，里面有我们的通关文书。你们必须把我们的行李带回来，这样我们才能继续我们的旅途。”

“我去，”猪回答说。“我以前去过花果山。我认识路。”

“不，”唐僧回答。“那只猴子不喜欢你。你说的话常常很粗鲁。他可能会很生气，会攻击你。”然后他转向沙悟净说，“沙，你必须去。找到那个猴子。如果他愿意把行李给你，就拿着，然后回到这里。如果他拒绝，不要和

tā zhēnglùn huò zhàndòu. Qù Pǔtuóluòjiā Shān, bǎ yíqiè dōu gàosù Guānyīn púsà, qǐng tā bāngmáng. Wǒmen zài zhèlǐ děngzhe."

Shā Wùjìng zǒu le sān tiān, lái dào le dōng dàhǎi. Tā wén dào yán shuǐ de wèidào, gǎnjué dào dàhǎi de fēng. Tā fēi guò dàhǎi, hěn kuài jiù dào le Huāguǒ Shān. Wǎng xià kàn, tā kàndào Sūn Wùkōng zhèng zuò zài yíkuài gāo gāo de shítou shàng, sìzhōu wéizhe xǔduō hóuzi. Shā cóng yún shàng xiàlái, lái dào dìshàng.

Sūn Wùkōng mǎshàng dà jiào, "Zhuā zhù tā!" Jǐ shí zhī hóuzi wéizhe Shā, zhuā tā de shǒubì hé tuǐ, suǒyǐ tā bùnéng dòng. Tāmen bǎ tā tái dào Sūn Wùkōng miànqián, Sūn Wùkōng shuō, "Nǐ shì shuí, méiyǒu wǒ de xǔkě, jiù lái dào wǒ de shāndòng?"

"Wǒ shì nǐ de dìdi, Shā Wùjìng. Wǒmen de shīfu duì nǐ hěn shēngqì, duì nǐ yòng le jǐn tóu dài mó yǔ. Wǒ hé nǐ de Zhū dìdi méiyǒu xiǎng yào zǔzhǐ tā. Nǐ qiú tā tíngzhǐ shuō nàge mó yǔ, dàn tā jùjué le. Ránhòu nǐ yòng nǐ de bàng dǎ tā, fēi dào zhèlǐ. Rúguǒ nǐ méiyǒu duì wǒmen shēngqì, jiù gēn wǒ huíqù. Wǒmen jiāng

他争论或战斗。去普陀洛迦山，把一切都告诉观音菩萨，请她帮忙。我们在这里等着。”

沙悟净走了三天，来到了东大海。他闻到盐[24]水的味道，感觉到大海的风。他飞过大海，很快就到了花果山。往下看，他看到孙悟空正坐在一块高高的石头上，四周围着许多猴子。沙从云上下来，来到地上。

孙悟空马上大叫，“抓住他！”几十只猴子围着沙，抓他的手臂和腿，所以他不能动。他们把他抬到孙悟空面前，孙悟空说，“你是谁，没有我的许可，就来到我的山洞？”

“我是你的弟弟，沙悟净。我们的师父对你很生气，对你用了紧头带魔语。我和你的猪弟弟没有想要阻止他。你求他停止说那个魔语，但他拒绝了。然后你用你的棒打他，飞到这里。如果你没有对我们生气，就跟我回去。我们将

---

[24] 盐 yán – salt

yìqǐ jìxù wǒmen de xīyóu. Dàn rúguǒ nǐ hái zài shēngqì, jiù bǎ xínglǐ gěi wǒ. Nǐ kěyǐ liú zài zhèlǐ, xiǎngshòu nǐ de lǎonián shēnghuó."

"Xiōngdì, nǐ bù dǒng. Wǒ bùxiǎng hé nǐmen, hái yǒu shīfu yìqǐ xíngzǒu. Wǒ juédìng zìjǐ qù xītiān. Wǒ yào qù Léiyīn Shān, wèn fózǔ yào shèng shū, wǒ huì bǎ tāmen sòng dào Táng huángdì nàlǐ. Wǒ de míngzì jiāng yìzhí liúchuán xiàqù!"

"Gēge, nǐ yǒuxiē bù míngbái. Fózǔ gàosùguò Guānyīn púsà, zài dōngfāng zhǎo yí wèi sēngrén, tā jiāng zǒuguò qiān zuò shān, lái dào xītiān. Zài lǚtú zhōng yù dào xǔduō máfan shì héshang de mìngyùn, zhè jiùshì wèishénme wǒmen sān gè rén dōu cóng jiānyù zhōng bèi fàng chūlái, ràng wǒmen hé tā yìqǐ xīyóu. Fózǔ yídìng bú huì bǎ shèng shū gěi nǐ yígè rén."

"A, dàn wǒ zhèlǐ shì yǒu yígè Táng héshang. Wǒ hái yǒu lìngwài liǎng gè túdì xiōngdì. Hóuzimen, gěi tā kàn kàn!" Xiǎo hóuzi dài chū le yì pǐ báimǎ. Qímǎ de shì yígè Tángsēng. Zhàn zài tā

一起继续我们的西游。但如果你还在生气，就把行李给我。你可以留在这里，享受你的老年生活。”

“兄弟，你不懂。我不想和你们、还有师父一起行走。我决定自己去西天。我要去雷音山，问佛祖要圣书，我会把它们送到唐皇帝那里。我的名字将一直留传下去！”

“哥哥，你有些不明白。佛祖告诉过观音菩萨，在东方找一位僧人，他将走过千座山，来到西天。在旅途中遇到许多麻烦是和尚的命运[25]，这就是为什么我们三个人都从监狱中被放出来，让我们和他一起西游。佛祖一定不会把圣书给你一个人。”

“啊，但我这里是有一个唐和尚。我还有另外两个徒弟兄弟。猴子们，给他看看！”小猴子带出了一匹白马。骑马的是一个唐僧。站在他

[25] 命运　　mìngyùn – fate, destiny

pángbiān de shì yígè Zhū Bājiè hé yígè Shā Wùjìng.

Shā kàndào zhè, biàn dé fēicháng fènnù. "Lǎo Shā zǒu bù gǎi míngzì, zuò bù gǎi xìng. Bú huì yǒu lìng yígè xiàng wǒ de rén!" Ránhòu tā yòng tā de guǎizhàng jī zhòng dì èr gè Shā, mǎshàng shā sǐ le tā. Sǐ le de Shā de shēntǐ biàn chéng le mó hóu jīng. Sūn Wùkōng hé qítā de hóuzi wéi zhù Shā, kāishǐ hé tā zhàndòu. Shā fēikuài de fēi zǒu le, tā duì zìjǐ shuō, "Wǒ yào mǎshàng jiàn púsà!"

Yìtiān yíyè hòu, tā lái dào le Pǔtuóluòjiā Shān. Tā màn màn de cóng yún shàng xiàlái. Mùchā jiàn le tā, wèn tā, "Shā Wùjìng, nǐ wèishénme zài zhèlǐ? Nǐ yīnggāi hé Tángsēng zài yìqǐ, bāngzhù tā qù xītiān!"

"Wǒ yào jiàn púsà!" Shā huídá.

Mùchā dài tā qù jiàn Guānyīn. Guānyīn púsà zhèng zuò zài zǐzhú lín de mùtou píngtái shàng. Píngtái xià zuòzhe Sūn Wùkōng. Tā duì tā zìjǐ shuō, "Táng héshang yídìng shì yù dào le máfan, zhè jiùshì wèishénme Shā zài zhèlǐ."

旁边的是一个猪八戒和一个沙悟净。

沙看到这，变得非常愤怒。“老沙走不改名字，坐不改姓。不会有另一个像我的人！”然后他用他的拐杖击中第二个沙，马上杀死了他。死了的沙的身体变成了魔猴精。孙悟空和其他的猴子围住沙，开始和他战斗。沙飞快地飞走了，他对自己说，“我要马上见菩萨！”

一天一夜后，他来到了普陀洛迦山。他慢慢地从云上下来。木叉见了他，问他，“沙悟净，你为什么在这里？你应该和唐僧在一起，帮助他去西天！”

“我要见菩萨！”沙回答。

木叉带他去见观音。观音菩萨正坐在紫竹林的木头平台[26]上。平台下坐着孙悟空。他对他自己说，“唐和尚一定是遇到了麻烦，这就是为什么沙在这里。”

---

[26] 平台 píngtái – platform

Shā zǒu jìn píngtái. Tā dǎsuàn gàosù Guānyīn tā de gùshi. Kě zài tā xiǎng yào shuōhuà qián, tā xiàng píngtái xià kàn, kàndào le zuò zài nàlǐ de Sūn Wùkōng. Tā mǎshàng xiǎng yòng tā de guǎizhàng dǎ nà zhī hóuzi, dà jiào dào, "Nǐ zhège wúfǎwútiān de hóuzi! Nǐ xiǎng yào shā sǐ wǒmen de shīfu! Nǐ zěnme gǎn lái zhèlǐ, piàn púsà?" Sūn Wùkōng zhǐshì zǒu dào yìbiān, duǒ kāi le zhè yī gōngjī.

"Tíng!" Guānyīn shuō. "Wùjìng, nǐ rúguǒ duì zhè zhī hóuzi yǒu yìjiàn, gàosù wǒ. Bié dǎ tā."

Shā fàngxià tā de guǎizhàng. Tā xiàng Guānyīn kētóu, bǎ yíqiè dōu gàosù le tā, cóng Sūn Wùkōng shā le liǎng gè qiángdào shǒulǐng kāishǐ, dào Huāguǒ Shān zhàndòu de shì.

"Wùjìng, nǐ cuòguài rén le. Zhè sì tiān lái, Sūn Wùkōng yìzhí hé wǒ zài yìqǐ. Wǒ méiyǒu ràng tā qù rènhé dìfāng."

Kěshì wǒ zài Huāguǒ Shān jiàn dào tā! Nǐ juédé wǒ zài shuōhuǎng

沙走近平台。他打算告诉观音他的故事。可在他想要说话前，他向平台下看，看到了坐在那里的孙悟空。他马上想用他的拐杖打那只猴子，大叫道，“你这个无法无天的猴子！你想要杀死我们的师父！你怎么敢来这里，骗菩萨？”孙悟空只是走到一边，躲开[27]了这一攻击。

“停！”观音说。“悟净，你如果对这只猴子有意见[28]，告诉我。别打他。”

沙放下他的拐杖。他向观音磕头，把一切都告诉了她，从孙悟空杀了两个强盗首领开始，到花果山战斗的事。

“悟净，你错怪[29]人了。这四天来，孙悟空一直和我在一起。我没有让他去任何地方。”

可是我在花果山见到他！你觉得我在说谎

---

27 躲开　duǒ kāi – to avoid

28 意见　yìjiàn – opinion (Chinese people say “do you have an opinion on this?” instead of “do you have a problem with this?”)

29 怪　guài – to blame

ma?"

"Qǐng búyào shēngqì. Nǐ hé Wùkōng yídìng yào yìqǐ qù Huāguǒ Shān kàn kàn. Huǎnghuà huì bèi huǐ diào, dàn zhēnxiàng huì liú xià." Suǒyǐ, Sūn Wùkōng hé Shā Wùjìng yìqǐ fēi dào le Huāguǒ Shān qù zhǎo chū zhēnxiàng.

吗？”

“请不要生气。你和悟空一定要一起去花果山看看。谎话会被毁掉[30]，但真相会留下。”所以，孙悟空和沙悟净一起飞到了花果山去找出真相。

[30] 毁掉　　huǐ diào – to destroy

Dì 58 Zhāng

Sūn Wùkōng de jīndǒu yún bǐ Shā zài yún shàng fēi yào kuài dé duō. Hěn kuài, tā jiù yuǎn yuǎn de zǒu zài Shā de qiánmiàn. "Màn diǎn," Shā shuō, "búyào shìzhe zài wǒ zhīqián dào nàlǐ, yě búyào zài wǒ kàndào nàlǐ fāshēng de shìqing zhīqián gǎibiàn nàlǐ de shìqing." Suǒyǐ Sūn Wùkōng màn le xiàlái, hé Shā yìqǐ zǒu.

Jīngguò yìtiān yíyè de fēixíng, tāmen lái dào le Huāguǒ Shān. Wǎng xià kàn, tāmen kànjiàn yígè Sūn Wùkōng zhèng zuò zài yíkuài gāo gāo de shítou shàng. Tā kàn shàngqù hé lìng yígè Sūn Wùkōng zhǎng dé yíyàng. Tā tóu shàng dàizhe yígè jīn tóu dài, zōngsè máofà, zuànshí yǎnjīng, yì zhāng zhǎngzhe dàyá de máo liǎn. Tā chuānzhe yí jiàn sīchóu chènshān, yìtiáo yòng hǔ pí zuò de duǎn qúnzi, yìshuāng lù pí xuēzi. Tā shǒu lǐ názhe yì gēn Jīn Gū Bàng.

Zhēn de Sūn Wùkōng dà hǎn dào, "Nǐ zěnme gǎn kàn shàngqù xiàng wǒ de yàngzi, zhuā wǒ de xiǎo hóuzi, zuò zài wǒ de shāndòng lǐ? Shì shì wǒ de bàng!" Jiǎ Sūn Wùkōng méiyǒu shíjiān huídá. Tā jǔ qǐ le

第 58 章

孙悟空的筋斗云比沙在云上飞要快得多。很快，他就远远的走在沙的前面。“慢点，”沙说，“不要试着在我之前到那里，也不要在我看到那里发生的事情之前改变那里的事情。”所以孙悟空慢了下来，和沙一起走。

经过一天一夜的飞行[31]，他们来到了花果山。往下看，他们看见一个孙悟空正坐在一块高高的石头上。他看上去和另一个孙悟空长得一样。他头上戴着一个金头带，棕色毛发，钻石眼睛，一张长着大牙的毛脸。他穿着一件丝绸衬衫，一条用虎皮做的短裙子，一双鹿皮靴子。他手里拿着一根金箍棒。

真的孙悟空大喊道，“你怎么敢看上去像我的样子，抓我的小猴子，坐在我的山洞里？试试我的棒！”假孙悟空没有时间回答。他举起了

---

[31] 飞行 fēixíng – flying

tā zìjǐ de bàng. Tāmen kāishǐ zhàndòu. Shī zhōng shuō,

Liǎng gēn tiě bàng

Liǎng zhī zhàndòu de hóuzi

Zhè chǎng zhàndòu búshì jiàn xiǎoshì!

Liǎng gè dōu xiǎng xīyóu

Zhēn hóu gēnzhe fó

Jiǎ hóu bù gēn rènhé rén

Tāmen liǎng gè dōu yǒu qiángdà de mófǎ

Tāmen zhàndòu de jìshù yíyàng

Tāmen zài dòng lǐ kāishǐ zhàndòu

Dàn hěn kuài shàng dào kōngzhōng

Tāmen zhàndòu le hěn cháng shíjiān, dàn méi yígè néng yíng

Shā kànzhe liǎng zhī zhàndòu de hóuzi. Tā xiǎng bāngzhù Sūn Wùkōng, dàn bù zhīdào nǎge shì zhēn, nǎge shì jiǎ. Tā zhǎo shìqing zuò, tā lái dào le dìshàng, shā le xiǎo mó hóu. Ránhòu tā zá huài le suǒyǒu de shítou jiājù. Ránhòu tā qù zhǎo xínglǐ, dàn méiyǒu zhǎodào, yīnwèi xínglǐ bèi cáng zài Shuǐ Lián Dòng de pùbù hòumiàn. Zuìhòu, tā yòu fēi dào le yún shàng, jìxù kànzhe zhàndòu.

他自己的棒。他们开始战斗。诗中说，

> 两根铁棒
>
> 两只战斗的猴子
>
> 这场战斗不是件小事！
>
> 两个都想西游
>
> 真猴跟着佛
>
> 假猴不跟任何人
>
> 他们两个都有强大的魔法
>
> 他们战斗的技术一样
>
> 他们在洞里开始战斗
>
> 但很快上到空中
>
> 他们战斗了很长时间，但没一个能赢

沙看着两只战斗的猴子。他想帮助孙悟空，但不知道哪个是真，哪个是假。他找事情做，他来到了地上，杀了小魔猴。然后他砸坏了所有的石头家具。然后他去找行李，但没有找到，因为行李被藏在水帘洞的瀑布后面。最后，他又飞到了云上，继续看着战斗。

"Shā," qízhōng yì zhī hóuzi hǎndào, "huíqù gàosù shīfu zhèlǐ de qíngkuàng. Ràng lǎo hóuzi hé zhège móguǐ zhàndòu. Wǒ huì bǎ tā dài qù Pǔtuóluòjiā Shān, ràng Guānyīn rènchū zhēn jiǎ."

Lìng yì zhī hóuzi hǎndào, "Shā, huíqù gàosù shīfu zhèlǐ de qíngkuàng. Ràng lǎo hóuzi hé zhège móguǐ zhàndòu. Wǒ huì bǎ tā dài qù Pǔtuóluòjiā Shān, ràng Guānyīn rènchū zhēn jiǎ."

Liǎng zhī hóuzi tīng qǐlái wánquán yíyàng, kàn qǐlái yě wánquán yíyàng. Shā bù zhīdào yīnggāi zěnme zuò, suǒyǐ tā zhào liǎng zhī hóuzi gàosù tā de qù zuò. Tā huíqù xiàng Tángsēng bàogào.

Kōngzhōng de zhàndòu hái zài jìxù. Liǎng zhī hóuzi yòng tāmen de jīndǒu yún fēi dào le Pǔtuóluòjiā Shān, yí lùshàng dōu zài zhàndòu. Tāmen lái dào le Pǔtuóluòjiā Shān. Mùchā jìnrù Guānyīn de shāndòng, gàosù tā, "Púsà, liǎng gè Sūn Wùkōng gāng dào. Tāmen zài zhàndòu."

Guānyīn líkāi tā de dòng qù kàn tāmen, Mùchā hé tā de lìng yígè túdì Shàncái gēnzhe tā. Qízhōng yì zhī hóuzi duì tā shuō, "Púsà, zhège móguǐ xiàng wǒ, dàn tā shì jiǎ de. Wǒmen de zhàndòu

“沙，”其中一只猴子喊道，“回去告诉师父这里的情况。让老猴子和这个魔鬼战斗。我会把他带去普陀洛迦山，让观音认出真假。”

另一只猴子喊道，“沙，回去告诉师父这里的情况。让老猴子和这个魔鬼战斗。我会把他带去普陀洛迦山，让观音认出真假。”

两只猴子听起来完全一样，看起来也完全一样。沙不知道应该怎么做，所以他照两只猴子告诉他的去做。他回去向唐僧报告。

空中的战斗还在继续。两只猴子用他们的筋斗云飞到了普陀洛迦山，一路上都在战斗。他们来到了普陀洛迦山。木叉进入观音的山洞，告诉她，“菩萨，两个孙悟空刚到。他们在战斗。”

观音离开她的洞去看他们，木叉和她的另一个徒弟善财跟着她。其中一只猴子对她说，“菩萨，这个魔鬼像我，但他是假的。我们的战斗

cóng Huāguǒ Shān kāishǐ, yìzhí jìxù dào zhèlǐ. Wǒ hěn nán dǎbài zhège jiǎ de. Shā kàn bùchū zhēn jiǎ, suǒyǐ tā bùnéng bāng wǒ. Qǐng bāngzhù nǐ de túdì. Fēnchū zhēn jiǎ, shuōchū zhēnxiàng!"

Ránhòu lìng y zhǐ hóuzi shuō le yíyàng de huà.

Guānyīn kàn le kàn tāmen, ránhòu tā shuō, "Nǐmen bié dǎ le. Fēnkāi zhàn, ràng wǒ kàn kàn nǐmen." Tāmen tíngzhǐ le zhàndòu, zhànzhe kànzhe tā. Tā ràng Mùchā zhuāzhù qízhōng yígè, ràng Shàncái zhuāzhù lìng yígè. Ránhòu tā niàn le jǐn tóu dài mó yǔ. Liǎng zhī hóuzi dōu jiào le qǐlái, shuāngshǒu bào tóu. Tāmen kāishǐ zài dìshàng dǎgǔn, tóngshí hái zài xiāng dòu.

Guānyīn duì tāmen shuō, "Sūn Wùkōng!" Liǎng rén dōu tíngzhǐ le zhàndòu, kànzhe tā. "Wǔbǎi nián qián, nǐ zài tiānshàng zhǎo le dà máfan. Tiāngōng lǐ suǒyǒu de dàrén dōu rènshí nǐ. Xiànzài qù nàlǐ, ràng tāmen gàosù nǐmen nǎ yígè shì zhēn de, nǎ yígè shì jiǎ de."

Liǎng gè Sūn Wùkōng dōu xiè le tā, ránhòu fēi dào le nán tiānmén, yí

从花果山开始，一直继续到这里。我很难打败这个假的。沙看不出真假，所以他不能帮我。请帮助你的徒弟。分出真假，说出真相！”

然后另一只猴子说了一样的话。

观音看了看他们，然后她说，“你们别打了。分开站，让我看看你们。”他们停止了战斗，站着看着她。她让木叉抓住其中一个，让善财抓住另一个。然后她念了紧头带魔语。两只猴子都叫了起来，双手抱头。他们开始在地上打滚[32]，同时还在相斗。

观音对他们说，“孙悟空！”两人都停止了战斗，看着她。“五百年前，你在天上找了大麻烦。天宫里所有的大人都认识你。现在去那里，让他们告诉你们哪一个是真的，哪一个是假的。”

两个孙悟空都谢了她，然后飞到了南天门，一

[32] 打滚　　dǎgǔn – to roll around

lù zhàndòu. Tāmen fēi guò dàmén, yìzhí fēi dào le Yùhuáng Dàdì de gōngdiàn. Sì wèi tiānshàng de dàshī jiàn tāmen lái le, duì huángdì shuō, "Dìqiú shàng de liǎng gè Sūn Wùkōng lái le. Tāmen zài zhàndòu. Tāmen xiǎngjiàn bìxià." Kěshì zài tāmen shuō wán zhīqián, liǎng zhī zhàndòu de hóuzi jiù fēi jìn le gōngdiàn, zài huángdì miànqián de dìshàng gǔn lái gǔn qù.

Huángdì dītóu kànzhe tāmen, qīngshēng wèn, "Nǐmen wèishénme méiyǒu xǔkě jiù lái dào zhèlǐ, zài wǒ miànqián zhàndòu? Nǐmen liǎng gè shì zài zhǎosǐ ma?"

Qízhōng yìrén shuō, "Bìxià! Bìxià! Duìbùqǐ, máfan nǐ le, zhège móguǐ yǐjīng biàn chéng le wǒ de yàngzi..." ránhòu tā jiāng shìqing de jīngguò gàosù le Yùhuáng Dàdì. Zài tā shuō wán hòu, lìng yì zhī hóuzi shuō le yíyàng de huà.

Huángdì duì tā de púrén shuō, "Bǎ Zhàoyāo Jìng ná lái!" Tāmen ná lái le mó jìng. Tā kànzhe jìngzi lǐ de liǎng zhī hóuzi. Liǎng zhī hóuzi cóng jìngzi lǐ kàn tā, tāmen kàn shàngqù shì yíyàng de. Tā duì tāmen shuō, "Wǒ bùnéng bāng nǐmen. Mǎshàng líkāi zhèlǐ."

路战斗。他们飞过大门，一直飞到了玉皇大帝的宫殿。四位天上的大师见他们来了，对皇帝说，“地球上的两个孙悟空来了。他们在战斗。他们想见陛下。”可是在他们说完之前，两只战斗的猴子就飞进了宫殿，在皇帝面前的地上滚来滚去。

皇帝低头看着他们，轻声问，“你们为什么没有许可就来到这里，在我面前战斗？你们两个是在找死吗？”

其中一人说，“陛下！陛下！对不起，麻烦你了，这个魔鬼已经变成了我的样子…”然后他将事情的经过告诉了玉皇大帝。在他说完后，另一只猴子说了一样的话。

皇帝对他的仆人说，“把照妖镜拿来！”他们拿来了魔镜。他看着镜子里的两只猴子。两只猴子从镜子里看他，他们看上去是一样的。他对他们说，“我不能帮你们。马上离开这里。”

Gǔn chū gōngdiàn, yí lùshàng dōu zài zhàndòu, tāmen duìzhe lìng yígè shuō, "Wǒ yào qù jiàn shīfu!"

Huí dào dìqiú shàng, Shā Wùjìng yǐjīng huí dào le Tángsēng hé Zhū zhù de xiǎo péng wū. Tā gàosù tāmen, "Wǒ qù le Huāguǒ Shān. Zài nàlǐ, wǒ kàndào le Sūn Wùkōng. Hái kàndào le yígè Zhū, yígè Shā hé yígè qízhe báimǎ de shīfu. Wǒ shā le Shā, kàndào nà shì mó hóu jīng. Ránhòu wǒ qù jiàn Guānyīn. Dāng dào tā jiā de shíhòu, zhēn de Sūn Wùkōng jiù zài nàlǐ. Wǒmen yìqǐ huí dào le Huāguǒ Shān. Liǎng zhī hóu wáng jiàn le miàn, jiù kāishǐ zhàndòu. Wǒ kàn bùchū zhēn jiǎ, suǒyǐ jiù huí dào zhèlǐ."

Tā de huà gāng jiéshù, tāmen jiù tīngdào le yígè hěn xiǎng de shēngyīn. Tāmen táitóu kàn xiàng tiānkōng. Tāmen jiàn liǎng zhī hóu wáng zài dà hǎn dà jiào, zài zhàndòu. Zhū shuō, "Ràng wǒ kàn kàn, shì búshì néng fēnchū tāmen." Tā fēi xiàng kōngzhōng, xiàngzhe tāmen fēi qù.

Liǎng gè Sūn Wùkōng dōu duìzhe Zhū dà hǎn, "Xiōngdì, kuài lái bāng wǒ dǎ zhège móguǐ!"

Zài xiàmiàn de xiǎo péng wū lǐ, nǚrénmen kàndào liǎng zhī hóuzi zài kōng

滚出宫殿，一路上都在战斗，他们对着另一个说，“我要去见师父！”

回到地球上，沙悟净已经回到了唐僧和猪住的小棚屋。他告诉他们，“我去了花果山。在那里，我看到了孙悟空。还看到了一个猪、一个沙和一个骑着白马的师父。我杀了沙，看到那是魔猴精。然后我去见观音。当到她家的时候，真的孙悟空就在那里。我们一起回到了花果山。两只猴王见了面，就开始战斗。我看不出真假，所以就回到这里。”

他的话刚结束，他们就听到了一个很响的声音。他们抬头看向天空。他们见两只猴王在大喊大叫，在战斗。猪说，“让我看看，是不是能分出他们。”他飞向空中，向着他们飞去。

两个孙悟空都对着猪大喊，“兄弟，快来帮我打这个魔鬼！”

在下面的小棚屋里，女人们看到两只猴子在空

zhōng zhàndòu. Yígè rén shuō, "Èn, zhèlǐ yídìng yǒu hěnduō rén! Wǒ bìxū ná chū gèng duō de shíwù." Tā kāishǐ zhǔnbèi mǐfàn hé chá. Lìng yígè nǚrén shuō, "Wǒ xīwàng tāmen kěyǐ tíngzhǐ zhàndòu. Wǒ pà tāmen huì gěi tiānshàng hé rénjiān dài lái hěn dà de máfan."

Shā shuō, "Nǎinai, bié dānxīn." Ránhòu duì Tángsēng shuō, "Shīfu, wǒ qù ràng tāmen èr gè tíngzhǐ zhàndòu. Zhū hé wǒ huì bǎ tāmen dài guòlái, nǐ kěyǐ jiějué zhè shì." Tā fēi dào kōngzhōng, shuō, "Nǐmen liǎng gè, xiànzài tíngzhǐ zhàndòu. Shīfu yào jiàn nǐmen liǎng gè." Tāmen dōu tíngzhǐ le zhàndòu, fēi dào le dìshàng. Tāmen zhàn zài wūwài, děngzhe.

Tángsēng ràng Zhū zhuā qízhōng de yì zhī hóuzi, ràng Shā zhuā lìng yì zhī. Ránhòu tā niàn jǐn tóu dài mó yǔ. Liǎng zhī hóuzi dōu jiào le qǐlái, yòng shǒu bào zhù tāmen de tóu. Tángsēng tíng le xiàlái. "Wǒ bùnéng fēn chū nǐmen liǎng gè," tā shuō.

Liǎng zhī hóu zǐ tóngshí shuō, "Xiōngdìmen, zhàogù hǎo shīfu. Wǒ yào qù jiàn Yánluó Wáng." Liǎng rén fēi qù jiàn Yánluó Wáng.

中战斗。一个人说，“嗯，这里一定有很多人！我必须拿出更多的食物。”她开始准备米饭和茶。另一个女人说，“我希望他们可以停止战斗。我怕他们会给天上和人间带来很大的麻烦。”

沙说，“奶奶，别担心。”然后对唐僧说，“师父，我去让他们二个停止战斗。猪和我会把他们带过来，你可以解决这事。”他飞到空中，说，“你们两个，现在停止战斗。师父要见你们两个。”他们都停止了战斗，飞到了地上。他们站在屋外，等着。

唐僧让猪抓其中的一只猴子，让沙抓另一只。然后他念紧头带魔语。两只猴子都叫了起来，用手抱住他们的头。唐僧停了下来。“我不能分出你们两个，”他说。

两只猴子同时说，“兄弟们，照顾好师父。我要去见阎罗王。”两人飞去见阎罗王。

Tāmen zǒu hòu, Zhū wèn Shā wèishénme bù bǎ xínglǐ cóng Huāguǒ Shān dài huílái. "Wǒ méi kàndào xínglǐ," Shā huídá.

"Nǐ bù zhīdào, pùbù de hòumiàn, shì yígè jiào Shuǐ Lián Dòng de mìmì shāndòng. Nà shì Sūn Wùkōng zhù de dìfāng. Wǒ xiǎng tā bǎ wǒmen de xínglǐ fàng zài nàlǐ le. Zhè shì wǒ qù ná xínglǐ de hǎo shíhòu."

"Xiǎoxīn yìdiǎn, xiōngdì," Shā shuō. "Yǒu yìqiān duō zhī mó hóu shǒuwèizhe shāndòng."

"Búyòng dānxīn wǒ!" Zhū dà xiào, tā fēi qù le Huāguǒ Shān.

Liǎng zhī zhàndòu de hóuzi lái dào le zài Yīn Shān de dìyù. Dìyù lǐ de guǐshén kàndào le tāmen de dàolái. Xià huài le, tāmen xiǎng duǒ qǐlái. Jǐ rén pǎo jìn le Hēi'àn Diàn, duì dìyù lǐ de shí gè dàwáng shuō, "Dàwáng, yǒu liǎng wèi Qí Tiān Dàshèng lái le. Tāmen xiàng liǎng zhī fènnù de lǎohǔ yíyàng zài zhàndòu." Shí gè dàwáng dōu lái dào le Hēi'àn Diàn. Tāmen jiào lái le dìyù lǐ suǒyǒu de shìbīng, qù zhuā nà liǎng zhī hóuzi. Tāmen děng zài hēi'àn zhōng. Hěn kuài, tāmen jiù gǎndào yízhèn hěn qiáng de lěngfēng, liǎng zhī zhàndòu de hóuzi dǎo

他们走后，猪问沙为什么不把行李从花果山带回来。“我没看到行李，”沙回答。

“你不知道，瀑布的后面，是一个叫水帘洞的秘密山洞。那是孙悟空住的地方。我想他把我们的行李放在那里了。这是我去拿行李的好时候。”

“小心一点，兄弟，”沙说。“有一千多只魔猴守卫着山洞。”

“不用担心我！”猪大笑，他飞去了花果山。

两只战斗的猴子来到了在阴山的地狱。地狱里的鬼神看到了他们的到来。吓坏了，他们想躲起来。几人跑进了黑暗殿，对地狱里的十个大王说，“大王，有两位齐天大圣来了。他们像两只愤怒的老虎一样在战斗。”十个大王都来到了黑暗殿。他们叫来了地狱里所有的士兵，去抓那两只猴子。他们等在黑暗中。很快，他们就感到一阵很强的冷风，两只战斗的猴子倒

zài dìshàng, gǔn lái gǔn qù, tīzhe yǎozhe lìngwài yígè.

Shí gè dàwáng zhōng zuì wěidà de Yánluó Wáng duì tāmen shuō, “Nǐmen liǎng gè wèishénme yào lái wǒ de wángguó zhǎo máfan?”

Qízhōng yì zhī hóuzi tī kāi le lìng yì zhī. Tā zhàn qǐlái, shuō, “Bìxià, wǒ zhèng gēnzhe Tángsēng zài qù xītiān de lǚtú shàng. Wǒmen bèi yìqún qiángdào gōngjī. Wǒ shā le tāmen jǐ gè rén. Wǒ shīfu hěn shēng wǒ de qì, ràng wǒ líkāi. Wǒ qù jiàn Guānyīn púsà, qǐngqiú tā de bāngzhù. Dāng wǒ zài nàlǐ de shíhòu, zhège móguǐ,” tā zhǐzhe lìng yì zhī hóuzi, “biàn chéng le wǒ de yàngzi, qù le wǒ zài Huāguǒ Shān de jiā. Tā yào zìjǐ qù xītiān jiàn fózǔ, zìjǐ qù ná shèng shū. Wǒ xiǎng yào zǔzhǐ tā, dàn wǒ méiyǒu bànfǎ yíng tā, yīnwèi tā hé wǒ shì yíyàng de. Méiyǒu rén néng fēnchū wǒmen. Wǒ wènguò Yùhuáng Dàdì, Guānyīn púsà hé wǒ shīfu, tāmen dōu bùnéng bāng wǒ.”

Lìng yì zhī hóuzi děng tā shuō wán, ránhòu shuō le wánquán yíyàng de huà, měi gè zì dōu yíyàng.

Yánluó Wáng ràng tā de yí wèi dàchén ná lái Shēngsǐ Bù. Zhè běn shū lǐ

在地上，滚来滚去，踢着咬着另外一个。

十个大王中最伟大的阎罗王对他们说，“你们两个为什么要来我的王国找麻烦？”

其中一只猴子踢开了另一只。他站起来，说，“陛下，我正跟着唐僧在去西天的旅途上。我们被一群强盗攻击。我杀了他们几个人。我师父很生我的气，让我离开。我去见观音菩萨，请求她的帮助。当我在那里的时候，这个魔鬼，”他指着另一只猴子，“变成了我的样子，去了我在花果山的家。他要自己去西天见佛祖，自己去拿圣书。我想要阻止他，但我没有办法赢他，因为他和我是一样的。没有人能分出我们。我问过玉皇大帝、观音菩萨和我师父，他们都不能帮我。”

另一只猴子等他说完，然后说了完全一样的话，每个字都一样。

阎罗王让他的一位大臣拿来生死簿。这本书里

miàn yǒu suǒyǒu shēngwù de míngzì — rén, hóuzi hé dòngwù. Shū zhōng yǒu yì zhāng shì tèbié jièshào tiānshàng chūshēng de shí hóuzi. Nà yì zhāng zhǐyǒu yí yè zhǐ, dàn bèi huà diào le. Yánluó Wáng duì liǎng gè hóuzi shuō, "Wǒ bùnéng bāng nǐmen."

Dàn jiù zài liǎng zhī hóuzi yào líkāi qián, Dìzàng púsà shuō, "Děng děng. Ràng wǒ wèn wèn Dìtīng, kěnéng tā kěyǐ bāngzhù wǒmen."

Dìtīng shì zhù zài Dizàng púsà zhuōzi xià de yì zhī dòngwù. Duì dìyù, rénjiān hé tiānshàng de yíqiè shēngwù, tā dōu néng mǎshàng kànchū zhēn jiǎ. Nà dòngwù cóng zhuōzi xià chūlái. Tā zǐxì de kànzhe nà liǎng zhī hóuzi. Ránhòu duì dàwángmen shuō, "Wǒ zhīdào shuí shì móguǐ, shuí shì Tángsēng de túdì. Dàn wǒ bùnéng gàosù nǐmen."

"Wèishénme bùnéng?" Dizàng wèn.

面有所有生物的名字一人、猴子和动物。书中有一章是特别介绍天上出生的石猴子。那一章只有一页纸，但被划掉了[33]。阎罗王对两个猴子说，“我不能帮你们。”

但就在两只猴子要离开前，地藏菩萨[34]说，“等等。让我问问谛听，可能他可以帮助我们。”

谛听是住在地藏菩萨桌子下的一只动物。对地狱、人间和天上的一切生物，他都能马上看出真假。那动物从桌子下出来。他仔细地看着那两只猴子。然后对大王们说，“我知道谁是魔鬼，谁是唐僧的徒弟。但我不能告诉你们。”

“为什么不能？”地藏问。

---

[33] Five hundred years earlier, Sun Wukong visited the underworld. He crossed out his own name and the names of 130 other monkeys from the Book of Long Life. This story is told in "*Trouble in Heaven*."

[34] Also known by his Sanskrit name Ksitigarbha, he is the Bodhisattva of all beings in the underworld. He has taken a vow to not achieve Buddhahood until all hells are emptied.

"Rúguǒ wǒ shuō le nǎ yígè shì móguǐ, tā huì zài zhèlǐ zàochéng hěn dà de máfan. Tā hé Sūn Wùkōng yíyàng qiángdà. Tā kěyǐ huǐ diào Hēi'àn Diàn, shā sǐ wǒmen suǒyǒu rén. Wǒmen méiyǒu tā nàme qiángdà qù dǎbài tā."

"Wǒmen néng zuò xiē shénme?"

Dìtīng zhǐshì shuō, "Fófǎ wúbiān."

Liǎng zhī hóuzi dōu tiào qǐlái jiào dào, "Shì a! Wǒ yào qù Léiyīn Shān jiàn fózǔ!" Kànzháo liǎng zhī hóu zǐ fēi zài kōngzhōng, líkāi dìyù, yí lùshàng dōu zài zhàndòu, Hēi'àn Diànzhōng de dàrénmen dōu fàngsōng le xiàlái.

Liǎng zhī hóuzi hěn kuài jiù dào le xītiān de Léiyīn Shān. Jǐ qiān gè héshang hé nígū zhèngzài tīng fózǔ jiǎngkè. Tā de kè jiǎng de shì guānyú zhēn hé jiǎ, kōng hé bù kōng, zhī hé wúzhī. Ránhòu fózǔ shuō, "Nǐmen dōu shì yìxīn. Dàn xiànzài kàn kàn xiāng dòu de èr xīn."

“如果我说了哪一个是魔鬼，他会在这里造成很大的麻烦。他和孙悟空一样强大。他可以毁掉黑暗殿，杀死我们所有人。我们没有他那么强大去打败他。”

“我们能做些什么？”

谛听只是说，“佛法无边[35]。”

两只猴子都跳起来叫道，“是啊！我要去雷音山见佛祖！”看着两只猴子飞在空中，离开地狱，一路上都在战斗，黑暗殿中的大人们都放松了下来。

两只猴子很快就到了西天的雷音山。几千个和尚和尼姑[36]正在听佛祖讲课。他的课讲的是关于真和假，空和不空，知和无[37]知。然后佛祖说，“你们都是一心。但现在看看相斗的二心[38]。”

---

[35] 无边　　wúbiān – limitless, boundless

[36] 尼姑　　nígū – nun

[37] 无　　wú – without

[38] In Buddhism, “monkey mind” (心猿) refers to the restless and uncontrolled mind of the untrained person.

Héshang hé nígū men táitóu kàn, kàndào le liǎng zhī zhàndòu de hóuzi. Bā wèi Jīngāng Wáng xiǎng yào zǔzhǐ tāmen jìnlái, dà hǎn dào, "Nǐmen liǎng gè yào qù nǎlǐ?"

Yì zhī hóuzi shuō, "Yāoguài jīng biàn chéng le wǒ de yàngzi, wǒ yào qǐng wěidà de fózǔ shuōchū zhēn jiǎ." Ránhòu tā jiǎng le zhěnggè gùshi. Děng tā shuō wán, lìng yì zhī hóuzi yě shuō le yíyàng de huà.

Tāmen děngzhe fózǔ shuōhuà. Kě jiù zài tāmen děng de shíhòu, yì duǒ fěnhóng sè de yún chūxiàn le, Guānyīn cóng yún zhōng zǒu le chūlái. Fózǔ xiàozhe duì tā shuō, "Guānyīn, nǐ néng shuōchū nǎge shì zhēn de, nǎge shì jiǎ de ma?"

"Wǒ shìguò le, dàn wǒ bùnéng. Suǒyǐ wǒ cái lái dào zhèlǐ, qiú nǐ lái zuò, bāngzhù Tángsēng wánchéng tā de lǚtú."

Fózǔ yòu xiào le, shuō, "Nǐ yǒu hěnduō de zhīshi, nǐ kěyǐ kàn dé hěn yuǎn, dànshì nǐ bù kěnéng zhīdào suǒyǒu de shìqing. Yǒu

和尚和尼姑们抬头看，看到了两只战斗的猴子。八位金刚王想要阻止他们进来，大喊道，“你们两个要去哪里？”

一只猴子说，“妖怪精变成了我的样子，我要请伟大的佛祖说出真假。”然后他讲了整个故事。等他说完，另一只猴子也说了一样的话。

他们等着佛祖说话。可就在他们等的时候，一朵粉红色的云出现了，观音从云中走了出来。佛祖笑着对她说，“观音，你能说出哪个是真的，哪个是假的吗？”

“我试过了，但我不能。所以我才来到这里，求你来做，帮助唐僧完成他的旅途。”

佛祖又笑了，说，“你有很多的知识[39]，你可以看得很远，但是你不可能知道所有的事情。有

[39] 知识 zhīshì – knowledge

wǔ zhǒng shénxiān, yǒu wǔ zhǒng shēngwù. Zhè rén búshì tāmen zhōng de rènhé yígè."

Guānyīn děngzhe, fózǔ zàicì shuōhuà, "Dànshì, yǒu sì zhǒng hóuzi, tā búzài nà shí zhǒng zhōng. Dì yī zhǒng shì tiānshàng chūshēng de shí hóu, tā hěn qiángdà, kěyǐ gǎibiàn xīngxing hé xíngxīng de guǐjì. Dì èr zhǒng shì fèifèi, zhīdào rén de shìqing, zhīdào yīn hé yáng. Dì sān zhǒng shì chángbìyuán, tā néng ná tàiyáng hé yuèliang, huǐ diào qiān zuò dàshān. Dì sì zhǒng shì liù ěr míhóu, tā zhīdào guòqù hé wèilái, zhīdào suǒyǒu de shìqing. Zhège jiǎ Wùkōng yídìng shì liù ěr míhóu, yīnwèi tā zhīdào qiānlǐ wài de shì."

Dāng fózǔ shuō zhè huà de shíhòu, jiǎ Sūn Wùkōng xià dé fādǒu. Tā

五种神仙，有五种生物[40]。这人不是他们中的任何一个。”

观音等着，佛祖再次说话。“但是，有四种猴子，它不在那十种中。第一种是天上出生的石猴，它很强大，可以改变星星和行星的轨迹[41]。第二种是狒狒[42]，知道人的事情，知道阴和阳。第三种是长臂猿[43]，它能拿太阳和月亮，毁掉千座大山。第四种是六耳猕猴[44]，它知道过去和未来，知道所有的事情。这个假悟空一定是六耳猕猴，因为他知道千里外的事[45]。”

当佛祖说这话的时候，假孙悟空吓得发抖。他

[40] The five kinds of immortals are the celestial, the earthbound, the divine, the human, and the ghostly. The five kinds of creatures are the short haired, the long haired, the scaly, the winged, and the crawling.

[41] 轨迹 guǐjì – path, trajectory

[42] 狒狒 fèifèi – baboon

[43] 长臂猿 chángbìyuán – gibbon

[44] 猕猴 míhóu – macaque

[45] According to Lam (2005) and McClanahan (2020), this six-eared macaque is actually the Macaque King named “Great Sage Informing Wind,” another one of Sun Wukong’s sworn brothers from his younger days, but for some reason Sun Wukong does not recognize him. Its six ears represent the ears of a third party eavesdropping without permission on the Buddha’s secret teaching.

tiào qǐlái xiǎng yào fēi zǒu. Fózǔ ràng jǐ qiān gè héshang hé nígū wéi zhù tā. Zhēn de Sūn Wùkōng pǎo guòqù bāngmáng, dànshì fózǔ duì tā shuō, "Wùkōng, bié dòng. Ràng wǒ bāng nǐ zhuā zhù tā."

Jiǎ Sūn Wùkōng biàn chéng yì zhī mìfēng, zhí fēi dào kōngzhōng. Fózǔ jiāng yígè jīnsè de yàofàn de wǎn rēng xiàng kōngzhōng. Tā zhuā zhù le mìfēng, bǎ tā fàng dào le dìshàng. Suǒyǒu de héshang hé nígū dōu yǐwéi mìfēng yǐjīng táozǒu le, dàn fózǔ shuō, "Bù, yāoguài jīng méiyǒu táozǒu. Kàn!" Tā jǔ qǐ yàofàn de wǎn. Zài wǎn de xiàmiàn shì yì zhī liù ěr míhóu.

Sūn Wùkōng jǔ qǐ tā de jīn gū bàng, zá zài míhóu shēnshàng, mǎshàng jiàng tā shā sǐ le. Fózǔ duì zhè hěn bù gāoxìng, dàn tā zhǐshì kànzhe Sūn Wùkōng shuō, "Xiànzài shì nǐ huí dào nǐ shīfu nàlǐ qù de shíhòu le. Nǐ bìxū zài tā de lǚtú shàng bāngzhù tā."

Sūn Wùkōng xiàng fózǔ kòutóu, huídá shuō, "Wěidà de fózǔ, wǒ bìxū gàosù nǐ, wǒ de shīfu bùxiǎng wǒ huí dào tā shēnbiān. Tā búyào wǒ de bāngzhù. Qǐng bǎ wǒ tóu shàng de tóu dài qǔ xiàlái, ràng wǒ huí dào wǒ guòqù zài Huāguǒ Shān shàng de shēnghuó."

跳起来想要飞走。佛祖让几千个和尚和尼姑围住他。真的孙悟空跑过去帮忙，但是佛祖对他说，“悟空，别动。让我帮你抓住他。”

假孙悟空变成一只蜜蜂，直飞到空中。佛祖将一个金色的要饭的碗扔向空中。它抓住了蜜蜂，把它放到了地上。所有的和尚和尼姑都以为蜜蜂已经逃走了，但佛祖说，“不，妖怪精没有逃走。看！”他举起要饭的碗。在碗的下面是一只六耳猕猴。

孙悟空举起他的金箍棒，砸在猕猴身上，马上将它杀死了。佛祖对这很不高兴，但他只是看着孙悟空说，“现在是你回到你师父那里去的时候了。你必须在他的旅途上帮助他。”

孙悟空向佛祖叩头，回答说，“伟大的佛祖，我必须告诉你，我的师父不想我回到他身边。他不要我的帮助。请把我头上的头带取下来，让我回到我过去在花果山上的生活。”

"Búyào zài húshuō le, búyào zài zhǎo máfan le," Fózǔ shuō, "Guānyīn huì dài nǐ huí dào nǐ shīfu nàlǐ. Tā bú huì bǎ nǐ tuī kāi. Děng nǐmen de lǚtú jiéshù hòu, nǐ jiāng zuò zài liánhuā bǎozuò shàng."

Guānyīn bǎ tā de liǎng zhī shǒuzhǎng fàng zài yìqǐ. Liǎng rén shàng dào yún shàng, fēi huí dào le Tángsēng hé Shā Wùjìng děngzhe de xiǎo péng wū. Tā duì Tángsēng shuō, "Qǐng nǐ búyào shēng Sūn Wùkōng de qì. Tā méiyǒu dǎ nǐ. Shì yígè jiǎ Sūn Wùkōng, yì zhī liù ěr míhóu zuò de. Fózǔ ràng wǒmen kàndào le zhēn jiǎ Wùkōng de bùtóng. Ránhòu zhēn de Sūn Wùkōng shā sǐ le jiǎ Sūn Wùkōng. Nǐ de lǚtú hái méiyǒu jiéshù, lùshàng hái yǒu xǔduō wéixiǎn děngzhe nǐ. Nǐ zài lǚtú zhōng xūyào Sūn Wùkōng de bǎohù. Qǐng bǎ tā dài huíqù."

Tángsēng xiàng tā jūgōng, zhǐshì shuō, "Wǒ zhào nǐ shuō de zuò."

Méiyǒu hěnjiǔ, Zhū jiù názhe xínglǐ cóng Huāguǒ Shān huílái le. Tā kàndào Guānyīn, xiàng tā kòutóu. Tā bǎ Léiyīn Shān fāshēng de yíqiè dōu gàosù le tā. Ránhòu Tángsēng hé sān gè túdì dōu xiàng Guānyīn jūgōng gǎnxiè. Tā huí dào le tā zài nánhǎi de jiā. Yóurénmen xiè le

“不要再胡说了，不要再找麻烦了，”佛祖说，“观音会带你回到你师父那里。他不会把你推开。等你们的旅途结束后，你将坐在莲花宝座上。”

观音把她的两只手掌放在一起。两人上到云上，飞回到了唐僧和沙悟净等着的小棚屋。她对唐僧说，“请你不要生孙悟空的气。他没有打你。是一个假孙悟空，一只六耳猕猴做的。佛祖让我们看到了真假悟空的不同。然后真的孙悟空杀死了假孙悟空。你的旅途还没有结束，路上还有许多危险等着你。你在旅途中需要孙悟空的保护。请把他带回去。”

唐僧向她鞠躬，只是说，“我照你说的做。”

没有很久，猪就拿着行李从花果山回来了。他看到观音，向她叩头。她把雷音山发生的一切都告诉了他。然后唐僧和三个徒弟都向观音鞠躬感谢。她回到了她在南海的家。游人们谢了

zhàogù tāmen de liǎng wèi fùrén. Ránhòu tāmen líkāi le xiǎo péng wū, jìxù tāmen de xīyóu.

照顾他们的两位妇人。然后他们离开了小棚屋，继续他们的西游。

The Angry Monkey

*** Chapter 56 ***

My dear child, tonight I will tell you another story about the monk Tangseng and his three disciples, the monkey king Sun Wukong, the pig-man Zhu Bajie, and the quiet but powerful man Sha Wujing. You remember that in last night's story they escaped from the cave of a scorpion monster. After that, they continued on their journey to the western heaven to acquire holy scriptures and bring them back to the Tang Empire.

Spring had turned into summer. The travelers walked slowly westward along the Silk Road. They saw yellow birds flying above them, and they could smell fragrant flowers on the warm breezes.

One day in early summer they arrived at a large mountain. The path went upwards and became more difficult. They climbed the mountain. The air became cooler. They saw wild animals on both sides of the path. Far away they heard the sound of a tiger's roar.

After climbing for several hours they reached the top of the mountain and began to travel down the western side. Tangseng's horse was very tired and began to walk slowly. Tangseng could not make the horse walk faster. Zhu shouted at it but the horse ignored him. Sun Wukong said, "Let me do it." He waved his golden hoop rod at the horse and shouted at it. Immediately the horse began to run. The Tang monk was frightened and held on tightly with both hands. The horse ran for twenty miles, taking Tangseng far ahead of his three disciples. Finally the horse came to level ground. It stopped running and began to walk again.

Tangseng had been very frightened while the horse was running. When the horse began walking again he relaxed and looked up. Ahead on the road he saw a group of about thirty men standing in the road. They all held swords, spears and long rods. One of the men had a green face, long teeth, and looked like a powerful dragon. Another had red hair, big eyes, and looked like an angry tiger. Tangseng could see that they were bandits.

"Where are you going?" asked the green-faced bandit chief. "We don't want to hurt you, we just want your travel money. Give it to me right now!"

Tanseng got down from his horse. He pressed his palms together and replied, "Great kings, this poor monk has been traveling for many years. Long ago I left the land of Tang. I am going to the western heaven to acquire holy scriptures. When I started my journey I had some money, but I spent it long ago. I ask you, great kings, to be kind and let me continue on my journey."

The bandit chief said, "We are guarding this road, and you must pay us. If you have no money, just give us your clothing and your horse. Then we will let you pass."

"This robe is old and threadbare. It is made of cloth begged from many different people. If you take it from me, it will be just like killing me. What will happen to you then? You might be a great king in this life, but in your next life you might return as an animal."

This made the bandit chief angry. He started to hit the monk with his rod. As the blows rained down on his head, Tangseng had an idea. He said, "Please stop hitting me. I have a young disciple who will arrive in a few minutes. He has a small bag of silver. I will tell him to give you the silver." The bandits stopped hitting Tangseng. They tied him up and hung him from a tree.

A short time later, the three disciples came near. Zhu looked and saw Tangseng hanging from a tree. "Look," he said, "our Master wanted to show us how strong he is, so he climbed a tree."

Using his diamond eyes, Sun Wukong saw the situation clearly. "You are a fool," he said to Zhu. "Stop talking. Wait here. I will go and see what's going on." He jumped up onto a small hill and looked again. Now he saw the bandits. He said to himself, "Ah, this is good. Business has come to my door!"

He shook his body and changed into a young monk about sixteen years old. He walked up to Tangseng and said, "Master, what's going on here? Who are these bad men?"

Tangseng cried, "Wukong, please save me! These are very bad men. They are bandits. They wanted money from me, but of course I had nothing to give them. So I told them that you were coming. I said that you would give them silver."

"Why did you tell them that?"

"I needed to make them stop hitting me!"

"Fine, fine. I like this. If you can keep doing this, Old Monkey will have lots of business!"

During this conversation the bandits quietly formed a circle around Sun Wukong. The green-faced bandit chief said, "Little monk, your master said that you had some money. Give it to us."

"No problem, I have quite a lot of gold and silver. But first you must let my master go." The bandit chief nodded his head, and a couple of the men released Tangseng. The monk ran to his white horse, jumped on the horse, and rode away as fast as he could. Sun Wukong started to follow him.

The bandit chief stopped him and said, "Where do you think you're going?"

Sun Wukong said, "All right, I will stay a little bit longer. But I think that the travel money should be divided in three parts."

The bandit chief laughed and said, "Ah, you are a clever little monk! You want some of the money for yourself, eh? All right then. Give us all your money and we will give you back a little bit. You can hide it in your robe and your master will never know."

"That's not quite what I meant," replied Sun Wukong. "What I meant was, bring out all the money that you have taken from other travelers. We will divide that money in three parts, two for me and one for you."

This made the bandits very angry. They all began to rain blows on Sun Wukong's head. Sun Wukong just stood without moving. The blows did not bother him at all. Finally he said, "Are you finished? Now I will show you something." He took a small needle from behind his ear and held it in his hand. "Change!" he whispered. Instantly the needle became his golden hoop rod, sixteen feet long and as thick as a rice bowl.

He put the rod on the ground and said, "If any of you can pick up this rod, you can keep it." The two bandit chiefs tried to pick it up, but it was like a fly trying to pick up a mountain. This was because the rod weighed thirteen thousand five hundred catties. Sun Wukong picked up the rod and said, "Now I'm afraid that your luck has just run out." He swung the rod twice, instantly killing both bandit chiefs. The rest of the bandits turned and ran for their lives.

Meanwhile, Tangseng was riding east as fast as he could towards the other two disciples. He reached Zhu and Sha and gasped, "Oh, disciples, go quickly to your elder brother. Tell him not to harm those poor bandits!"

Zhu ran toward Sun Wukong as fast as he could. He reached the monkey and said, "Elder brother, our master tells you not to kill any of the bandits."

"I have not killed anyone," replied Sun Wukong. He pointed to the two bandit chiefs lying dead on the ground and said, "These two are just sleeping."

"That's strange. Why are they sleeping in the middle of the road? Maybe they were awake all night drinking wine and singing songs." Zhu looked more closely. "And why are they sleeping with their mouths open?"

"That's because I hit them with my rod. They will never wake up."

"Ah, I understand," replied Zhu. He ran back to Tangseng and said, "Master, good news. The bandits have disbanded."

"That's good. Where did they go?"

"Two of them didn't go anywhere."

"Then why did you say they are disbanded?"

"They have been beaten to death. Isn't that disbanded enough for you?"

Tangseng was very angry when he heard this. "Zhu, use your rake to dig graves for these two. Then we will bury them. I will recite a prayer for the dead." Zhu started to use his rake to dig a hole. He dug about three feet down, then his rake struck some rocks. He dropped the rake and used his snout to quickly finish digging the graves. When he was finished, the holes were five feet deep. The disciples put the dead bandits in the holes, then covered them with dirt. Tangseng stood at the edge of the grave. He pressed his hands together and said,

"Brothers, I bow to you, please listen to my words
I come from the east, sent by the Tang Emperor
I met you here on this road, face to face
You wanted my clothing and my horse
I begged you to let me pass but you did not listen
You met my elder disciple and fell by his rod
Now I pity your dead bodies
If you meet Yama please remember
My elder disciple's name is Sun
My name is Chen
My other disciples are Bajie and Wujing
Tell Yama that Sun killed you, not us!"

Sun Wukong listened to this. When Tangseng was finished, he said, "Master, you are not being kind, are you? Yes, I killed these bandits. But I did it for you. This is your journey, I am just here to help you. If you had not decided to travel to the west, these men would not be dead. If you had not brought me as your disciple, these men would not be dead. This is your fault, not mine!" Then he turned to the graves and said angrily,

"Listen to me, you stupid bandits
You hit me on the head again and again

You made me very angry
Yes, killing you was a mistake
But I am not afraid of you
I am not afraid of Yama
I am the Great Sage Equal to Heaven
All ten Kings of the Underworld have served me
The Jade Emperor himself knows me
The guardian of Mount Tai fears me
All the gods of heaven are my friends
You may go to hell and complain about me
I don't care!"

Tanseng listened to this. He was surprised that Sun Wukong was so angry. "Disciple, my words were meant to help you see the value of life, and make you a better person. Why are you taking this so hard?"

"Master," replied Sun Wukong, "your words were no joke." He started walking westward, then he turned and added, "Let's find a place to stay tonight." Tangseng and the other two disciples followed him. All four of them were unhappy and a little bit angry. There was tension in the air.

Soon they arrived at a small village. Looking around, they saw that it was a nice place. They heard dogs barking and they saw candles burning in the windows of small homes. An old man came out from one of the houses. Tangseng greeted him. "Hello, grandfather. We are traveling to the western heaven to seek the Buddha's holy scriptures. It's getting late, and we were hoping to find a place to stay for the night. Please do not be afraid of my disciples. They are ugly but they will not hurt you."

The old man looked at the disciples. He said, "They are extremely ugly. One of them looks like a yaksa, one is a horse-face, and one is a thunder god."

Sun Wukong was still angry. He shouted back, "Old man, the thunder god is my grandson, the yaksa is my great-grandson, and the horse-face is my great-great-grandson." When he heard this the old man became very frightened. His face turned pale and he fell on the ground. Tangseng helped him to stand up, saying, "Don't worry my friend, they are all quite rude and don't know how to speak politely. The one you called a thunder god is my eldest disciple Sun Wukong. The one you called horse-face is my middle disciple Zhu Bajie. And the one you called a yaksa is my junior disciple Sha Wujing. They are not demons. Don't be afraid."

"All right, come in," said the old man. They entered his house. The old man asked his wife to bring tea. She went to the kitchen to make the tea. A small boy followed her.

"Grandfather," said Tangseng, "what is your good surname and how old are you?"

"My surname is Yang. I have lived for seventy four years. I have one son. The little child you see here is my grandson."

"I would like to meet your son," said Tangseng.

"That young man is unworthy of meeting a holy monk like you. I wish he had a good job. But he only wants to kill people and take their money. His friends are bad men. He went out five days ago and has not returned."

Tangseng thought about this. He was wondering if Sun Wukong had killed their son on the road earlier that day. Before he could say anything, Sun Wukong said to the old man, "Sir, such a bad son can only bring troubles to you and your family. Why keep him? Let me go and find him. I can kill him for you!"

"Perhaps I would let you do that, but I have no other son. It's true that my son has become a bad person, but I need someone to dig my grave when I die."

Before Sun Wukong could reply, Sha said quickly, "Elder brother, you should mind your own business." Turning to the old man, he said, "Grandfather, you and your family have been very kind to us. Please show us where we can sleep tonight." The old man led them out to the barn. He put some clean straw down on the ground for the travelers to sleep on. Soon all four were asleep.

Now, Yang's son was indeed one of the bandits but he was not one of the bandit chiefs. Earlier that day, after Sun Wukong killed the bandit chiefs, Yang's son and the other bandits ran for their lives. That night after the travelers had gone to bed, the bandits knocked on the door of the Yang house. The old man opened the door. The bandits ran into the house, shouting, "We're hungry!" The wife of Yang's son woke up. She started to cook some rice for the bandits. Yang's son went out to the back of the house to get some firewood. He saw Tangseng's white horse. He returned to the house and asked his father, "What is that white horse in back of the house?"

The old man replied, "The horse belongs to some traveling monks. They are going to the western heaven. They asked if they could sleep here tonight."

Yang's son clapped his hands and said to his friends, "Good news, my friends! Our enemies are here! We can kill them tonight. We can take their horse and their money."

One of the other bandits said, "Let's wait. First, let's have some dinner and sharpen our knives. Later tonight we can kill them." So they all sat down to eat dinner and sharpen their knives.

While they were eating dinner, the old man quietly went out to the barn. He woke up the travelers and told them that the bandits were planning to kill them. "Run away!" he said. The travelers picked up their luggage, left the barn, and headed west on the road.

Around the time of the fifth watch, the bandits decided it was time to attack. They ran out of the house and into the barn. But of course the travelers were gone. The bandits started running west on the road, carrying knives and spears. Soon they caught up with the travelers.

Sun Wukong stopped and turned to face the bandits. "Disciple," said Tangseng, "you must not hurt these people. Just frighten them and make them go away."

Sun Wukong ignored him. The bandits formed a circle around Sun Wukong. They started to attack him with knives and spears. The Monkey King began to swing his golden hoop rod, faster and faster. When he hit the bandits they fell like stars. A few escaped and a few were wounded, but most of them were killed. Their bodies lay dead on the ground.

Tangseng was very upset. He rode his horse away from the fight. Sun Wukong ran over to one of the wounded bandits and said, "Where is the son of Yang?" The bandit pointed to a man and said, "There, the one in yellow." Sun Wukong ran over to the one in yellow and cut off his head. Picking it up, he ran to Tangseng and said, "Master, here is the son of old man Yang. I have cut off his head."

Tangseng fell down on the ground and cried, "Take it away! Take it away!" Zhu kicked the head to the side of the road. Then he used his rake to dig a small hole and bury the head.

Sha went over to Tangseng and helped him to stand up. Tangseng began to recite the Tight Headband Spell. Immediately the headband on Sun Wukong's head became tighter. Sun Wukong cried out in pain. Tangseng said the Tight Headband Spell again and again and again. Ten times he said the spell. Ten times the headband became tighter. Sun Wukong was lying on the ground, his hands on his head, crying in pain, saying, "Master, please stop!"

Tangseng said to him, "I have nothing to say to you. I do not want you as my disciple anymore. Yang's son was no good, but he did not deserve to be killed by you. You have killed too many people and caused too much trouble. There is no kindness in you. Be gone, and don't come back!"

Sun Wukong held his head with both hands and cried, "Stop it!" Then he used his cloud somersault and disappeared.

***** Chapter 57 *****

Sun Wukong had to leave, but where could he go? He thought about going home to Flower Fruit Mountain, but he was afraid that the other monkeys would despise him for not serving his master. He thought about going to the palace in heaven, but he was afraid that the gods might not allow him to stay there. He thought about going to live with his friend the Dragon King of the Eastern Ocean, but he did not want to go there as a homeless monkey. Finally he decided to return to Tangseng and apologize.

He used his cloud somersault and came down in front of

Tangseng's horse, saying, "Master, please forgive me. I will not hurt or kill others anymore. I beg you to let me travel with you to the western heaven."

But Tangseng was still angry at Sun Wukong. He just started reciting the Tight Headband Spell again and again, twenty times. Now the headband was so tight that it cut an inch into Sun Wukong's flesh. Then Tangseng said, "Why are you bothering me again? Just go away."

"Master, you need my help. Without me I don't think you will reach the western heaven."

Tangseng replied, "You are a murdering ape. I don't want you anymore. Maybe I will reach the western heaven, maybe I will not, but it's no concern of yours. Leave now. If you don't, I will continue saying the Tight Headband Spell and I won't stop until you are dead."

Sadly, Sun Wukong rose into the clouds again. He decided to go to Potalaka Mountain and visit the Bodhisattva Guanyin.

An hour later he arrived at the Great Southern Ocean. He flew on to Potalaka Mountain, then entered the purple bamboo forest where Guanyin lived. Guanyin's disciple Moksha greeted him, saying, "Why has the Great Sage come here?"

"I have something to tell the Bodhisattva."

Moksha wanted to ask him some questions, but just then a beautiful white bird came into view. It flew back and forth. This mean that Guanyin was ready to see him. Sun Wukong approached Guanyin. He started to cry. Guanyin said, "Wukong, tell me why you are crying. I will help you."

"You set me free from my prison and set me on the path of

the Buddha. Since then I have accompanied the Tang monk, protecting him from monsters, demons and wild animals. How could I know that he would be so ungrateful? Truly, he cannot tell black from white."

Guanyin smiled and said, "Wukong, tell me more about black and white."

Sun Wukong told her everything. He told her about the bandits. He told her how Tangseng had used the Tight Headband Spell. And he told her that there was no place in Heaven or on earth where he could go now.

Guanyin listened. Then she said, "The Tang monk is a holy monk, he would not kill even one person. But you have killed many. It's ok for you to kill a demon or a monster, but you must not kill a person. You could have easily frightened those people away without killing them. In my opinion, you have acted badly."

"I understand. But I should not be treated this way. I beg you, please show some kindness. Please release me from this magic headband. Let me return to Flower Fruit Mountain where I can live in peace."

"I'm sorry but I cannot do that. The Buddha himself gave me this headband to give to you. He also taught me the Tight Headband Spell. But I'm afraid there is no Loose Headband Spell."

"All right, then. I thank you. I will leave now."

"Where will you go?"

"I will go to see the Buddha himself, and ask him to remove my headband." He got up and prepared to leave.

"No, wait. I want to look into the future for you."

"Please do not. I don't want to see my future."

"Not your future. The Tang monk's future." She closed her eyes, and looked into the three worlds. She opened her eyes and said, "Wukong, soon your master will face death. He will need you. I will tell him to take you back so that both of you may reach the end of your journey and acquire wisdom." Sun Wukong did not dare say anything.

While Sun Wukong was visiting with Guanyin, Tangseng and the other two disciples continued on their journey. By late afternoon Tangseng was getting very hungry. He asked Zhu to find a village nearby where he could beg some rice. Zhu looked but did not see any nearby village. Tangseng said, "Well then, please get me some water from the river. I am extremely thirsty." Zhu left to get some water.

Tangseng and Sha waited for a long time, but Zhu did not return. Finally, Sha left to get some water. Tangseng was now alone, sitting by the side of the road. He heard a loud noise and looked up. Sun Wukong stood in front of him holding a bowl of water, saying, "Master, I have returned. Here is some water. Drink!"

But Tangseng was still angry. He said, "I don't want your water and I don't want you. It will be better for me to die of thirst than to take you back. Get out of here now!" Sun Wukong became angry. He hit Tangseng, knocking him to the ground. Then he grabbed the luggage and used his cloud somersault to fly away.

Zhu was getting ready to get water from the river, but he looked up and saw a little hut. He decided to go there to beg some food. He didn't want to frighten people with his appearance so he recited a spell and shook his body several times. He changed into a sickly old monk with yellow skin.

"Please, please," he said to the door of the house, "I am a poor monk. Please give me some rice!" Two women were inside the house. They were afraid of the sickly monk, so they quickly filled his begging bowl with rice and gave it to him.

As Zhu was returning with the rice, he met Sha on the road. They poured the rice from the begging bowl into a fold of Zhu's robe, then they filled the begging bowl with water from the river. Then they returned to the place where they'd left Tangseng. But when they arrived at that place, they saw Tangseng lying on the ground, face down. He looked like he was dead. The luggage was gone.

"That's it, that's it!" cried Zhu. "We are finished. No more talk about going to get scriptures in the western heaven. You stay here and keep an eye on Master's body. I will go to the next town and buy a coffin so we can bury him. After that, we can both go home and forget about this journey."

Sha turned Tangseng's body over and he bent down to look more carefully. He saw that Tangseng was breathing a little bit. "Master is still alive!" said Sha.

They waited until Tangseng took a few more breaths and opened his eyes. He said to his disciples, "It was that lawless monkey. Soon after you left, the monkey returned. I told him to go away. He hit me and left me for dead."

They returned to the little hut where Zhu had begged rice earlier that day. One of the two women opened the door and said, "What, more traveling monks? I saw an old sickly monk earlier today and gave him some rice. I have nothing more to give you. Please go away and don't bother me."

Zhu told the woman that he was the sickly monk that she had seen. Then Tangseng explained that they were traveling to the western heaven, and that his senior disciple had hit him on the head and then run away. He asked if they could rest in her house. She agreed, and gave them some hot tea to drink. Tangseng drank the tea. After a while he felt better. He said to his disciples, "One of you must go and find that lawless monkey. He has our luggage which contains our travel rescript. You must bring back our luggage so we can continue our journey."

"I will go," replied Zhu. "I have been to Flower Fruit Mountain before. I know the way."

"No," replied the Tang monk. "That monkey does not like you. And your words are often rude. He might become angry and attack you." Then turning to Sha Wujing he said, "Sha, you must go. Find the monkey. If he is willing to give you the luggage, just take it and return here. If he refuses, do not argue or fight with him. Just go to Potalaka Mountain, tell everything to Bodhisattva Guanyin, and ask her for help. We will wait here."

Sha Wujing traveled for three days to arrive at the Great Eastern Ocean. He smelled the salt water and felt the ocean winds. He flew across the ocean and soon arrived at Flower Fruit Mountain. Looking down, he saw Sun Wukong sitting on a high rock, surrounded by many other monkeys. Sha came down from the clouds and landed on the ground.

Immediately Sun Wukong shouted, "Seize him!" Dozens of monkeys surrounded Sha and grabbed his arms and legs so he could not move. They carried him to Sun Wukong, who said, "Who are you, to approach my cave without my permission?"

"I am your younger brother, Sha Wujing. Our master was angry at you and used the Tight Headband Spell on you. Your brother Zhu and I did not try to stop him. You asked him to stop using the spell but he refused. Then you hit him with your rod and flew here. If you have no anger towards us, return with me. Together we will continue on our journey to the west. But if you are still angry, just give me the luggage. You can stay here and enjoy your old age."

"Brother, you don't understand. I don't want to travel with you and the Master. I have decided to go by myself to the western heaven. I will travel to Thunderclap Mountain, I will ask Buddha for the holy books, and I will deliver them to the Tang Emperor. My fame will last forever!"

"Elder brother, you are a little bit confused. The Buddha told the Bodhisattva Guanyin to find a monk in the eastern lands who would travel over a thousand mountains to reach the western heaven. It is the monk's fate to meet many troubles on the journey, that's why the three of us were released from our prisons and allowed to accompany him on the journey. The Buddha will never give the holy books to you alone."

"Ah, but I do have a Tang monk. And I have two other disciples. Monkeys, show him!" the little monkeys brought out a white horse. Riding the horse was a Tangseng. Standing next to him was a Zhu Bajie and a Sha Wujing.

Sha saw this and became furious. "Old Sand does not change his first name when he walks, he does not change his surname when he sits. There cannot be another like me!" Then he struck the second Sha with his staff, killing him instantly. The body of the dead Sha turned into a demon monkey spirit. Sun Wukong and the other monkeys surrounded Sha and started fighting with him. Sha flew away as fast as he could, saying to himself, "I need to see the Bodhisattva right away!"

A day and a night later he arrived at Potalaka Mountain. He came down slowly from the clouds. He was met by Moksha, who asked him, "Sha Wujing, why are you here? You should be with the Tang monk helping him to travel to the western heaven!"

"I must see the Bodhisattva!" replied Sha.

Moksha took him to see Guanyin. The Bodhisattva was sitting on a wooden platform in the purple bamboo forest. Underneath the platform sat Sun Wukong. He said to himself, "The Tang monk must be in trouble, that's why Sha is here."

Sha approached the platform. He planned to tell Guanyin his story. But before he could start, he looked under the platform and saw Sun Wukong sitting there. Instantly he tried to strike the monkey with his staff, shouting, "You lawless monkey! You tried to kill our Master! How dare you come here and try to fool the Bodhisattva?" Sun Wukong simply stepped aside, dodging the blow.

"Stop it!" said Guanyin. "Wujing, if you have a problem with this monkey, tell me. Don't hit him."

Sha put down his staff. He kowtowed to Guanyin and told her everything, starting with Sun Wukong killing the two bandit chiefs, and finishing with the story of the fight at Flower Fruit Mountain.

"Wujing, you are blaming the wrong person. Sun Wukong has been here with me for the last four days. I have not let him go anywhere."

"But I saw him at Flower Fruit Mountain! Do you think I am lying?"

"Please don't get upset. You and Wukong must go to Flower Fruit Mountain and take a look together. Lies will be destroyed but truth will remain." And so, Sun Wukong and Sha Wujing flew together to find the truth at Flower Fruit Mountain.

*** Chapter 58 ***

Sun Wukong's cloud somersault was much faster than Sha's cloud flying. Soon he was far ahead of Sha. "Slow down," said Sha, "Don't try to arrive before me and change things before I see what's going on." So Sun Wukong slowed down to travel next to Sha.

After a day and a night of flying they arrived at Flower Fruit Mountain. Looking down, they saw a Sun Wukong sitting on a high rock. He looked just like the other Sun Wukong. He had a gold headband on his head, brown hair, diamond eyes, a hairy face with huge teeth. He wore a silk shirt, a kilt made of tiger skin, and deerskin boots. In his hand he held a golden hoop rod.

The real Sun Wukong shouted, "How dare you look like me, capture my little monkeys, and sit in my cave? Taste my rod!" The false Sun Wukong did not have time to reply. He raised his own rod. They began to fight. The poem says,

> Two iron rods
> Two fighting monkeys
> This fight was no small thing!
> Both wanted to travel to the west
> The true monkey follows the Buddha

The false monkey follows no one
They both have powerful magic
Their fighting skills are equal
They start fighting at the cave
But soon rise into the air
They fight a long time but neither can win

Sha watched the two fighting monkeys. He wanted to help Sun Wukong but he could not tell which was the true and which was the false. Looking for something to do, he came down to the ground and killed the little monkey demons. Then he smashed all the stone furniture. Then he looked for the luggage but he could not find it, because the luggage was hidden behind a waterfall in Water Curtain Cave. Finally he flew up into the clouds again to continue watching the fight.

"Sha," shouted one of the monkeys, "go back to Master and tell him the situation. Let Old Monkey fight this demon. I will bring him to Potalaka Mountain and let Guanyin tell truth from false."

The other monkey shouted, "Sha, go back to Master and tell him the situation. Let Old Monkey fight this demon. I will bring him to Potalaka Mountain and let Guanyin tell truth from false."

Both monkeys sounded exactly the same and looked exactly the same. Sha did not know what to do, so he did what both monkeys told him to do. He returned to report to Tangseng.

The fight continued in the sky. The two monkeys used their cloud somersaults to fly to Potalaka Mountain, fighting all the way. They arrived at Potalaka Mountain. Moksha entered Guanyin's cave and told her, "Bodhisattva, two Sun Wukongs have just arrived. They are fighting."

Guanyin left her cave and went to see them, followed by Moksha and her other disciple Shancai. One of the monkeys said to her, "Bodhisattva, this demon resembles me but he is false. Our fight started on Flower Fruit Mountain and continues here. It is difficult for me to defeat this false one. Sha could not tell truth from false, so he could not help me. Please help your disciple. Tell truth from false, tell real from unreal!"

Then the other monkey said exactly the same thing.

Guanyin looked at them, then she said, "Both of you stop fighting. Stand apart, let me look at you." They stopped fighting and stood looking at her. She told Moksha to grab one of them and Shancai to grab the other. Then she recited the Tight Headband Spell. Both monkeys screamed and clutched their heads with their hands. They started rolling on the ground while still fighting each other.

Guanyin said to them, "Sun Wukong!" Both of them stopped fighting and looked at her. "Five hundred years ago you caused great trouble in heaven. All the great ones in heaven know you. Go there now, and let them tell which one of you is true and which is false."

The two Sun Wukongs both thanked her, then they flew up to the South Heaven Gate, fighting all the way. They flew through the gate and all the way to the palace of the Jade Emperor. The four masters of heaven saw them coming and said to the emperor, "Two Sun Wukongs from the land below have arrived. They are fighting. They want to see Your Majesty." But before they were finished speaking, the two fighting monkeys flew into the palace and rolled around on the floor in front of the emperor's throne.

The emperor looked down at them and asked quietly, "Why are you here without permission, fighting in front of me? Are you both seeking death?"

One of them said, "Your Majesty! Your Majesty! I am sorry for disturbing you, but this demon has taken my form…" and then he told the entire story to the Jade Emperor. When he was finished, the other monkey said exactly the same words.

The emperor said to his servants, "Bring me the Demon-Reflecting Mirror!" They brought the magic mirror. He looked in the mirror at the two monkeys. Both monkeys looked back at him from the mirror, looking exactly the same. He said to them, "I cannot help you. Leave this place at once."

Rolling out of the palace, fighting all the way, they said to each other, "I will go and see Master!"

Back on earth, Sha Wujing had returned to the little hut where Tangseng and Zhu were staying. He told them, "I went to Flower Fruit Mountain. There I saw Sun Wukong. I also saw a Zhu and a Sha and a Master on a white horse. I killed the Sha and saw that it was a monkey demon spirit. Then I went to see Guanyin. When I arrived at her home, the true Sun Wukong was there. We went together back to Flower Fruit Mountain. The two monkey kings saw each other and started to fight. I could not tell the true from the false, so I returned here."

Just as he finished speaking, they heard a loud sound. They looked up in the sky. They saw the two monkey kings shouting and fighting with each other. Zhu said, "Let me see if I can tell them apart." He flew into the air towards them.

Both Sun Wukongs shouted at Zhu, "Brother, come and help me fight this demon!"

Down below in the little hut, the women saw the two monkeys fighting in the sky. One said, "Well, there certainly are a lot of people here! I must bring out more food." She started preparing rice and tea. The other woman said, "I wish they would stop fighting. I fear that they will cause great trouble in heaven and on earth."

Sha said, "Don't worry, grandmother." Then he said to Tangseng, "Master, I will go up and tell these two to stop fighting. Zhu and I will bring them to you, and you can sort this out." Flying into the air, he said, "You two, stop fighting right now. Master wants to see both of you." They both stopped fighting and flew down to earth. They stood outside the house, waiting.

Tangseng told Zhu to grab one of the monkeys, and Sha to grab the other. He then recited the Tight Headband Spell. Both monkeys screamed and grabbed their heads with their hands. Tangseng stopped. "I cannot tell the two of you apart," he said.

The two monkeys said at the same time, "Brothers, take care of Master. I will go to see Yama, the King of the Underworld." The two of them flew off to see Yama.

After they left, Zhu asked Sha why he did not bring back the luggage from Flower Fruit Mountain. "I did not see it," replied Sha.

"You don't know that behind the waterfall is a secret cave called Water Curtain Cave. That's where the Monkey King lives. I think that he put our luggage there. This would be a good time for me to go and get the luggage."

"Be careful, brother," said Sha. "Over a thousand monkey

demons are guarding the cave."

"Don't worry about me!" laughed Zhu, and he flew away to Flower Fruit Mountain.

The two fighting monkeys arrived at the underworld, at the Mountain of Darkness. The spirits of the underworld saw them coming. Terrified, they tried to hide. A few ran into the Hall of Darkness and said to the Ten Kings of the Underworld, "Great Kings, there are two Great Sages Equal to Heaven coming. They are fighting like two angry tigers." The ten kings gathered in the Hall of Darkness. They called all the soldiers of the underworld to come and capture the two monkeys. They waited in the dark. Soon they felt a strong cold wind, and the two fighting monkeys fell to the floor and rolled around, kicking and biting each other.

Yama, the greatest of the ten kings, said to them, "Why are the two of you coming and causing trouble here in my kingdom?"

One of the monkeys kicked away the other one. He stood up and said, "Your Majesty, I was traveling with the Tang monk towards the western heaven. We were attacked by a group of bandits. I killed a few of them. My Master was angry with me and sent me away. I went to see the Bodhisattva Guanyin to ask her for advice. While I was there, this demon," and he pointed to the other monkey, "took my form and went to my home at Flower Fruit Mountain. He wants to go by himself to the western heaven to see the Buddha and take the holy books for himself. I tried to stop him but I cannot win a fight against him because he is my equal. Nobody can tell us apart. I have asked the Jade Emperor and the Bodhisattva Guanyin and my Master, but none of them can help me."

The other monkey waited until he finished, then he said the

exact same thing, word for word.

Yama called for one of his ministers to bring out the Long Life Book. This book has the names of all living beings in it – people, monkeys and animals. There was a special chapter in the book for heaven born stone monkeys. That chapter had only one page, but it was crossed out. Yama said to the monkeys, "I cannot help you."

But before the two monkeys could leave, the Bodhisattva Dizang said, "Wait. Let me ask Investigative Hearing, maybe he can help us."

Investigative Hearing was a beast who lived under the desk of the Bodhisattva Dizang. He can instantly see truth or false among all creatures of the underworld, the earthly world, and the heavenly worlds. The beast came out from under the desk. He looked carefully at the two monkeys. Then he said to the kings, "I know which one is the demon and which is the disciple of the Tang monk. But I cannot tell you."

"Why not?" asked Dizang.

"If I say which one is the demon, he will cause great trouble here. His powers are as great as Sun Wukong himself. He could destroy the Hall of Darkness and kill all of us. We are not strong enough to defeat him."

"What can we do?"

Investigative Hearing just said, "The Buddha's power has no limit."

Both monkeys jumped up and shouted, "Yes! I will go to Thunderclap Mountain and see the Buddha himself!" The great beings in the Hall of Darkness watched with relief as the two monkeys flew through the air, out of the Underworld, fighting all the way.

The two monkeys quickly arrived at Thunderclap Mountain in the western heaven. Thousands of monks and nuns were listening to a lecture by the Buddha. The lecture was about the real and the unreal, empty and non-empty, knowledge and non-knowledge. Then the Buddha said, "You all have one mind. But now look at two minds fighting against each other."

The monks and nuns looked up and saw the two fighting monkeys. The eight Golden Kings tried to stop them from entering, shouting, "Where do you two think you are going?"

One of the monkeys said, "A monster spirit has taken my appearance, I want to ask the great Buddha to tell the truth from the false." Then he told the entire story. When he was finished, the other monkey said the same thing.

They waited for the Buddha to speak. But while they waited, a pink cloud appeared, and Guanyin stepped out of the cloud. The Buddha smiled at her and said, "Guanyin, can you tell which is the true and which is the false?"

"I tried but I cannot. That is why I have come here, to beg you to do this, to help the Tang monk complete his journey."

The Buddha smiled again and spoke. "You have great knowledge and you can see very far, but you cannot know all things. There are five kinds of immortals and there are five kinds of creatures. This fellow is not any of those."

Guanyin waited, and the Buddha spoke again. "However, there are four kinds of monkeys which do not belong to any of these ten kinds. The first is the heaven-born stone monkey, it has great power and can change the path of the stars and planets.

The second is the baboon, it understands the affairs of humans and has knowledge of yin and yang. The third is the gibbon, it can grab the sun and moon and destroy a thousand mountains. And the fourth is the six-eared macaque, it has knowledge of past and future and understands all things. This false Wukong must be a six-eared macaque because he has knowledge of events a thousand miles away."

When the Buddha said this, the false Sun Wukong shook with fear. He jumped up and tried to fly away. The Buddha ordered the thousands of monks and nuns to encircle him. The true Sun Wukong ran to help, but the Buddha said to him, "Wukong, don't move. Let me capture him for you."

The false Sun Wukong changed into a bee and flew straight up into the air. The Buddha threw a golden begging bowl into the air. It caught the bee and brought it down to the ground. All the monks and nuns thought that the bee had escaped, but the Buddha said, "No, the monster spirit has not escaped. Look!" He lifted up the begging bowl. Under the bowl was a six-eared macaque.

Sun Wukong lifted his golden hoop rod and brought it down on the macaque, killing it instantly. The Buddha was not happy about this, but he simply looked at Sun Wukong and said, "Now it is time for you to return to your Master. You must help him on his journey."

Sun Wukong kowtowed to the Buddha and replied, "O great Buddha, I must tell you that my Master does not want me to return to him. He does not want my help. Please remove the headband from my head so that I can return to my old life on Flower Fruit Mountain."

"Stop this foolish talk and don't cause any more trouble," said the Buddha. "Guanyin will take you back to your Master. He will not turn you away. Later, when your journey is finished, you will sit on a lotus throne."

Guanyin pressed her palms together. The two of them rose up to the clouds and flew back to the little hut where Tangseng and Sha Wujing were waiting. She said to Tangseng, "Please don't be angry with Sun Wukong. He did not strike you. It was a false Sun Wukong, a six-eared macaque. The Buddha himself showed us the difference between the true and false Wukongs. Then the true Sun Wukong killed the false one. Your journey is not finished yet, and many dangers still wait for you on the path. You will need the protection of Sun Wukong on your journey. Please take him back."

Tangseng bowed to her and simply said, "I will do as you ask."

A short time later, Zhu returned from Flower Fruit Mountain with the luggage. He saw Guanyin and kowtowed to her. She told him the story of everything that had happened at Thunderclap Mountain. Then Tangseng and the three disciples all bowed to give thanks to Guanyin. She returned to her home in the South Sea. The travelers thanked the two women who had taken care of them. Then they left the little hut and continued on their journey to the west.

Proper Nouns

These are all the Chinese proper nouns used in this book.

Chinese	Pinyin	English
陈	Chén	Chen (Tangseng's surname)
地藏	Dízàng	Dizang (a name, literally "Earth Womb" or "Earth Storehouse")
谛听	Dìtīng	Investigative Hearing (a name, literally "Hear Truth")
东海龙王	Dōng Hǎi Lóngwáng	Dragon King of the Eastern Ocean
观音	Guānyīn	Guanyin (a bodhisattva)
黑暗殿	Hēi'àn Diàn	Mountain of Darkness
花果山	Huāguǒ Shān	Flower Fruit Mountain
金刚王	Jīngāng Wáng	Golden Kings
雷音山	Léiyīn Shān	Thunderclap Mountain
木叉	Mùchā	Moksha (a name)
普陀洛迦山	Pǔtuóluòjiā Shān	Potalaka Mountain
齐天大圣	Qí Tiān Dàshèng	Great Sage Equal to Heaven
沙悟净	Shā Wùjìng	Sha Wujing (a name)
善财	Shàncái	Shancai (a name)
生死簿	Shēngsǐ Bù	Long Life Book
水帘洞	Shuǐ Lián Dòng	Water Curtain Cave
丝绸之路	Sīchóu Zhīlù	Silk Road
孙悟空	Sūn Wùkōng	Sun Wukong (a name)
唐	Táng	Tang empire
唐僧	Tángsēng	Tangseng (a name)
泰山	Tàishān	Mount Tai
杨	Yáng	Yang (a name)
阎罗王	Yánluó Wáng	Yama, King of the Underworld
妖镜拿	Yāo Jìng Ná	Demon Reflecting Mirror
玉皇大帝	Yùhuáng Dàdì	Jade Emperor
猪八戒	Zhū Bājiè	Zhu Bajie (a name)

Glossary

These are all the Chinese words (other than proper nouns) used in this book.

Chinese	Pinyin	English
啊	a	ah, oh, what
安静	ānjìng	quietly
吧	ba	(indicates assumption or suggestion)
把	bǎ	(measure word for gripped objects)
八	bā	eight
爸爸	bàba	father
白	bái	white
百	bǎi	hundred
办法	bànfǎ	method
棒	bàng	rod, stick, wonderful
绑	bǎng	to tie
帮(助)	bāng (zhù)	to help
帮忙	bāngmáng	to help
抱(住)	bào (zhù)	to hold, to carry
报告	bàogào	report
保护	bǎohù	to protect
宝座	bǎozuò	throne
耙子	bàzi	rake
被	bèi	(passive particle)
笨	bèn	stupid
本	běn	(measure word for books)
比	bǐ	compared to, than
闭(上)	bì (shàng)	to shut, to close up
变	biàn	to change

变成	biànchéng	become
别	bié	do not
别人	biérén	other people
病	bìng	disease
陛下	bìxià	Your Majesty
必须	bìxū	must
鼻子	bízi	nose
布	bù	cloth
簿	bù	ledger book
不	bù	no, not, do not
不理	bù lǐ	to ignore
不错	búcuò	not bad
不配	búpèi	not worthy
不同	bùtóng	different
不想	bùxiǎng	don't want, in no mood
不在乎	búzàihū	not give a damn about
才	cái	only
才能	cáinéng	can only, ability, talent
苍蝇	cāngyíng	fly
草	cǎo	grass
茶	chá	tea
长	cháng	long
常	cháng	often
场	chǎng	(measure word for public events)
唱(歌)	chàng (gē)	to sing
长臂猿	chángbìyuán	gibbon
城(市)	chéng (shì)	city
成(为)	chéng (wéi)	to become
衬衫	chènshān	shirt
尺	chǐ	Chinese foot

吃(饭)	chī (fàn)	to eat
吃惊	chījīng	to be surprised
丑	chǒu	ugly
出	chū	out
喘气	chuǎn	to gasp
穿(着)	chuān (zhe)	to wear
窗(户)	chuāng (hù)	window
厨房	chúfáng	kitchen
春(天)	chūn (tiān)	spring
出生	chūshēng	born
出现	chūxiàn	to appear
次	cì	(measure word for time)
次	cì	next in a sequence
从	cóng	from
聪明	cōngmíng	clever
粗	cū	broad, thick
粗鲁	cūlǔ	rude
寸	cùn	Chinese inch
村(庄)	cūn (zhuāng)	village
村子	cūnzi	village
错	cuò	wrong
错怪	cuòguài	wrongly blamed
错误	cuòwù	mistake
大	dà	big
打	dǎ	to hit, to play
大多数	dà duōshù	most, majority
大喊	dà hǎn	to shout
打败	dǎbài	defeat
大臣	dàchén	minister
打滚	dǎgǔn	roll around

戴	dài	to wear
袋(子)	dài (zi)	bag
带(子)	dài (zi)	band, belt, ribbon
打开	dǎkāi	open
大门	dàmén	door
但(是)	dàn (shì)	but, however
当	dāng	when
挡(住)	dǎng (zhù)	to block
当然	dāngrán	certainly
担心	dānxīn	worry
道	dào	path, way, Dao, to say
到	dào	to arrive, towards
倒	dào	to pour
倒	dǎo	to fall
刀	dāo	knife
大人	dàrén	address adult male respectfully
大师	dàshī	grandmaster
打算	dǎsuàn	intend
大王	dàwáng	king
地	de	(adverbial particle)
的	de	of
得	dé	(particle showing degree or possibility)
得(到)	dé (dào)	to get
等	děng	to wait
第	dì	(prefix before a number)
地	dì	land, ground
殿	diàn	hall, temple
点	diǎn	point, hour
点头	diǎntóu	to nod
掉	diào	to fall, to fall out, to drop

吊	diào	to hang
弟弟	dìdi	younger brother
地方	dìfāng	place
帝国	dìguó	empire
地球	dìqiú	earth
敌人	dírén	enemy
低头	dītóu	head bowed
地狱	dìyù	hell, underworld
洞	dòng	cave, hole
动	dòng	to move
懂	dǒng	to understand
东	dōng	east
动物	dòngwù	animal
东西	dōngxi	thing
斗	dòu	fight
都	dōu	all
短	duǎn	short
对	duì	correct, towards someone
对不起	duìbùqǐ	sorry
对待	duìdài	to treat someone
朵	duǒ	(measure word for flowers and clouds)
躲	duǒ	to hide
多	duō	many
躲开	duǒ kāi	to avoid
多么	duōme	how
饿	è	hungry
嗯	en, èn	well, um
二	èr	two
耳(朵)	ěr (duo)	ear
儿子	érzi	son

饭	fàn	cooked rice
放	fàng	to put, to let out
房(子)	fang (zi)	house
放松	fàngsōng	to relax
放下	fàngxià	to lay down
饭碗	fànwǎn	rice bowl
发生	fāshēng	to occur
发现	fāxiàn	to find out
飞	fēi	to fly
非常	fēicháng	very much
狒狒	fèifèi	baboon
飞行	fēixíng	flying
份	fèn	(measure word for documents, meals, jobs)
分	fēn	to share, to divide
风	fēng	wind
粉红(色)	fěnhóng (sè)	pink
坟墓	fénmù	grave
愤怒	fènnù	anger
分钟	fēnzhōng	minute
佛	fó	~~monk~~ Buddha
佛法	fófǎ	Buddha's teachings
佛祖	fózǔ	Buddhist teacher
付	fù	to pay
妇(人)	fù (rén)	lady, madam
附近	fùjìn	nearby
盖	gài	cover, to cover
改(变)	gǎi (biàn)	to change
敢	gǎn	to dare
感(到)	gǎn (dào)	to feel

刚(才)	gāng (cái)	just, just a moment ago
干净	gānjìng	clean
感觉	gǎnjué	feel
感谢	gǎnxiè	to thank
告	gào	to sue, to complain about
高	gāo	tall, high
告诉	gàosù	to tell
高兴	gāoxìng	happy
个	gè	(measure word, generic)
哥哥	gēge	elder brother
给	gěi	to give
根	gēn	(measure word for long thin things)
跟(着)	gēn (zhe)	with, to follow
更	gèng	more
更	gēng	watch (2-hour period)
宫(殿)	gong (diàn)	palace
攻击	gōngjī	to attack
工作	gōngzuò	work, job
狗	gǒu	dog
谷仓	gǔ cāng	barn
怪	guài	to blame
拐杖	guǎizhàng	staff, crutch
棺材	guāncai	coffin
关于	guānyú	about
轨迹	guǐjī	trajectory, path
滚	gǔn	to roll
国	guó	country
过	guò	(after verb to indicate past tense)
过	guò	to pass
过夜	guòyè	to stay overnight

故事	gùshì	story
还	hái	still, also
海	hǎi	sea, ocean
害怕	hàipà	fear
还是	háishì	still is
孩子	háizi	child
喊(叫)	hǎn (jiào)	to call, to shout
喊道	hǎn dào	shouted
好	hǎo	good
和	hé	and, with
河	hé	river
喝	hē	drink
黑(色)	hēi (sè)	black
黑暗	hēi'àn	dark
很	hěn	very
和尚	héshang	monk
红(色)	hóng (sè)	red
后	hòu	after, back, behind
猴(子)	hóu (zi)	monkey
虎	hǔ	tiger
话	huà	word, speak
划掉	huà diào	to cross out
坏	huài	bad
还	huán	to return
黄(色)	huáng (sè)	yellow
皇帝	huángdì	emperor
谎话	huǎnghuà	lie
荒野	huāngyě	wilderness
花香	huāxiāng	floral scent
回	huí	to return

会	huì	will, to be able to
挥(动)	huī (dòng)	to swat, to wave
毁掉	huǐ diào	to destroy
回答	huídá	reply
活	huó	to live
或(者)	huò (zhě)	or
活着	huózhe	alive
胡说	húshuō	to babble, nonsense
猢狲	húsūn	ape
呼吸	hūxī	to breathe
几	jǐ	several
记(住)	jì (zhù)	to remember
击中	jī zhòng	to hit a target
假	jiǎ	fake
家	jiā	family, home
假的	jiǎ de	fake
家具	jiājù	furniture
件	jiàn	pieces (measure word)
剑	jiàn	sword
间	jiān	(measure word for clothing, matters)
见(面)	jiàn (miàn)	to see, to meet
讲	jiǎng	to speak
将	jiāng	shall
讲课	jiǎngkè	lecture
监狱	jiānyù	prison
叫	jiào	to call, to yell
教(会)	jiāo (huì)	to teach
叫醒	jiào xǐng	to wake up
家人	jiārén	family, family members
价值	jiàzhí	value

记得	jìdé	to remember
接(住)	jiē (zhù)	to catch
接近	jiējìn	close to
解决	jiějué	to solve, settle, resolve
解散	jiěsàn	disband
介绍	jièshào	introduction
解释	jiěshì	to explain
结束	jiéshù	end, finish
进	jìn	to enter
紧	jǐn	tight
斤	jīn	cattie (measure of weight)
金(色)	jīn (sè)	golden
金箍棒	jīn gū bàng	golden hoop
筋斗云	jīndǒu yún	cloud somersault
精	jīng	spirit
镜(子)	jìng (zi)	mirror
今天	jīntiān	today
技术	jìshù	skill, ability
就	jiù	just, right now
旧	jiù	old
救	jiù	to save, to rescue
久	jiǔ	long
继续	jìxù	continue
举(起)	jǔ (qǐ)	to lift
觉得	juédé	to feel
决定	juédìng	decide
鞠躬	jūgōng	to bow down
拒绝	jùjué	to refuse
开	kāi	to open
开始	kāishǐ	to begin

开玩笑	kāiwánxiào	to make joke
砍	kǎn	to cut
看	kàn (zhe)	to look
看起来	kàn qǐlái	it looks like
看上去	kàn shàngqù	it looks like
渴	kě	thirst
棵	kē	(measure word for trees, vegetables, some fruits)
可怜	kělián	pathetic
可能	kěnéng	possible
可是	kěshì	but
磕头	kētóu	to kowtow
可以	kěyǐ	can
空(气)	kōng (qì)	air, void, emptiness
口	kǒu	mouth
叩头	kòutóu	to kowtow
哭	kū	to cry
快	kuài	fast
困难	kùnnán	difficulty
来	lái	to come
来自	láizì	from
老	lǎo	old
老虎	lǎohǔ	tiger
老年	lǎonián	elderly
蜡烛	làzhú	candle
了	le	(indicates completion)
雷	léi	thunder
冷	lěng	cold
离	lí	away from, to leave
里(面)	li (miàn)	inside

俩	liǎ	both
脸	liǎn	face
莲(花)	lián (huā)	lotus
凉	liáng	cold
两	liǎng	two
离开	líkāi	to leave
礼貌	lǐmào	polite
林	lín	forest
另	lìng	other, another
另外	lìngwài	in addition
留	liú	keep
六	liù	six
留下	liú xià	to keep, to leave behind, to stay
龙	lóng	dragon
路	lù	road
绿(色)	lǜ (sè)	green
旅途	lǚtú	journey
吗	ma	(indicates a question)
马	mǎ	horse
麻烦	máfan	trouble
埋	mái	to bury
买	mǎi	to buy
慢	màn	slow
满	mǎn	full
矛	máo	spear
毛(发)	máo (fà)	hair
马上	mǎshàng	immediately
没	méi	no
每	měi	every
没关系	méiguānxì	it's ok, no problem

美丽	měilì	beautiful
没有	méiyǒu	no, not have
们	men	(indicates plural)
门	mén	door
面	miàn	side, surface, noodles
面对面	miànduìmiàn	face to face
米饭	mǐfàn	cooked rice
蜜蜂	mìfēng	bee
猕猴	míhóu	macaque
秘密	mìmì	secret
名(字)	míng (zì)	first name, name
明白	míngbái	clear
命运	mìngyùn	destiny, fate
磨	mó	to sharpen
魔(法)	mó (fǎ)	magic
魔鬼	móguǐ	demon
木(头)	mù (tou)	wood
拿	ná	to take
那	nà	that
奶奶	nǎinai	grandmother
那里	nàlǐ	there
哪里	nǎlǐ	where
那么	nàme	so
难	nán	difficult
男	nán	male
男孩	nánhái	boy
那样	nàyàng	like that
呢	ne	(indicates question)
能	néng	can
你	nǐ	you

你好	nǐ hǎo	hello
年	nián	year
念	niàn	to read aloud
念经	niànjīng	chanting
年轻	niánqīng	young
鸟	niǎo	bird
尼姑	nígū	nun
女	nǚ	female
哦	ó, ò	oh?, oh!
爬	pá	to climb
怕	pà	afraid
拍	pāi	to smack, to clap
旁	páng	beside
跑	pǎo	run
泡茶	pào chá	make tea
咆哮	páoxiāo	to roar
碰	pèng	to touch
棚屋	péng wū	hut, shack
朋友	péngyǒu	friend
匹	pǐ	(measure word for horses, cloth)
骗	piàn	to trick, to cheat
皮肤	pífū	leather, skin
平	píng	flat
平台	píngtái	platform
瀑布	pùbù	waterfall
仆人	púrén	servant
菩萨	púsà	bodhisattva, buddha
骑	qí	to ride
起	qǐ	from, up
前	qián	in front, before

钱	qián	money
千	qiān	thousand
强(大)	qiáng (dà)	strong, powerful
强盗	qiángdào	bandit
前往	qiánwǎng	go to
敲	qiāo	to knock
瞧不起	qiáobùqǐ	despise
悄悄	qiāoqiāo	quietly
气氛	qìfēn	atmosphere
奇怪	qíguài	strange
起来	qǐlái	(after verb, indicates start of an action)
亲爱的	qīn'ài de	dear
请	qǐng	please
轻风	qīng fēng	light breeze
情况	qíngkuàng	situation
请求	qǐngqiú	request
穷	qióng	poor (no money)
其他	qítā	other
求	qiú	to beg
其中	qízhōng	among them
妻子	qīzi	wife
去	qù	to go
取	qǔ	to take
圈	quān	~~to lock up~~ circle
群	qún	group or cluster
裙子	qún zi	kilt, skirt
让	ràng	to let, to cause
然后	ránhòu	then
人	rén	person, people
认出	rèn chū	to recognize

仁慈	réncí	kindness
认得	rèndé	to know, to recognize
扔	rēng	to throw
任何	rènhé	any
人间	rénjiān	human world
认识	rènshí	to understand
认为	rènwéi	to believe
容易	róngyì	easy
肉	ròu	meat, flesh
入	rù	to enter
如果	rúguǒ	if, in case
三	sān	three
僧(人)	sēng (rén)	monk
杀	shā	to kill
山	shān	mountain
山顶	shāndǐng	mountain top
上	shàng	on, up
伤(害)	shāng (hài)	hurt
伤心	shāngxīn	sad
烧	shāo	to burn
谁	~~shéi~~ shúi	who
深	shēn	deep
身(体)	shēn (tǐ)	body
神(仙)	shén (xiān)	spirit, god
身边	shēnbiān	around
圣(人)	shèng (rén)	saint, holy sage
声(音)	shēng (yīn)	sound
圣僧	shèng sēng	holy monk, Bodhisattva
生病	shēngbìng	sick
生活	shēnghuó	life

圣经	shèngjīng	holy scripture
生命	shēngmìng	life
生气	shēngqì	angry
生物	shēngwù	animal, creature
生意	shēngyì	business
声音	shēngyīn	sound
身后	shēnhòu	behind
什么	shénme	what
神奇	shénqí	magical
神仙	shénxiān	immortal
十	shí	ten
是	shì	is, yes
试	shì	to taste, to try
诗(歌)	shī (gē)	poetry
时(候)	shí (hòu)	time, moment, period
事(情)	shì (qing)	thing
石(头)	shí (tou)	stone
食(物)	shí (wù)	food
士兵	shìbīng	soldier
师父	shīfu	master
时间	shíjiān	time, period
尸体	shītǐ	dead body
手	shǒu	hand
手臂	shǒubì	arm
首领	shǒulǐng	chief, leader
受伤	shòushāng	injured
守卫	shǒuwèi	guard
手掌	shǒuzhǎng	palm
树	shù	tree
书	shū	book

双	shuāng	pair
水	shuǐ	water
睡(觉)	shuì (jiào)	to sleep
说(话)	shuō (huà)	to say
说谎	shuōhuǎng	lie
四	sì	four
死	sǐ	die
丝绸	sīchóu	silk
四周	sìzhōu	all around
松	sōng	loose
送(给)	sòng (gěi)	to give a gift
岁	suì	years of age
孙子	sūnzi	grandson
所以	suǒyǐ	so
所有	suǒyǒu	all
他	tā	he
它	tā	it
她	tā	she
抬	tái	lift
太	tài	too
躺	tǎng	lie down
逃(走)	táo (zǒu)	to escape
特别	tèbié	special
踢	tī	to kick
天	tiān	day, sky
天宫	tiāngōng	palace of heaven
天空	tiānkōng	sky
天上	tiānshàng	heaven, on the sky
条	tiáo	(measure word for narrow, flexible things)

跳	tiào	to jump
铁	tiě	iron
听	tīng	to listen
停(止)	tíng (zhǐ)	stop
听起来	tīng qǐlái	sound
痛(苦)	tòng (kǔ)	suffering
通关文书	tōngguān wénshū	travel rescript
同意	tóngyì	agree
头	tóu	head
头发	tóufà	hair
土	tǔ	dirt, earth
徒弟	túdì	apprentice
腿	tuǐ	leg
推开	tuī kāi	yìshēng
挖	wā	to dig
外	wài	outside
完	wán	to finish
万	wàn	ten thousand
碗	wǎn	bowl
晚	wǎn	late, night
弯	wān	bend
弯下腰	wān xiàyāo	to bend down (bend the waist)
完成	wánchéng	to complete
晚饭	wǎnfàn	dinner
王	wáng	king
往	wǎng	to
忘(记)	wàng (jì)	to forget
王国	wángguó	kingdom
完全	wánquán	complete

晚上	wǎnshàng	evening
位	wèi	(measure word for people, polite)
为	wèi	for
围(住)	wéi (zhù)	encircle, surround
伟大	wěidà	great
味道	wèidào	to taste, to smell
未来	wèilái	future
为什么	wèishénme	why
危险	wéixiǎn	danger
问	wèn	to ask
问好	wènhǎo	say hello
温暖	wēnnuǎn	warm
问题	wèntí	problem, question
我	wǒ	I, me
无	wú	without
五	wǔ	five
屋(子)	wū (zi)	house
无边	wúbiān	boundless
无法无天	wúfǎwútiān	lawless
西	xī	west
下	xià	down, under
吓	xià	to scare
先	xiān	first
像	xiàng	like, to resemble
向	xiàng	towards
响	xiǎng	loud
想	xiǎng	to want, to miss, to think of
相	xiāng	mutually
想要	xiǎng yào	want to
享受	xiǎngshòu	enjoy

先生	xiānshēng	sir, gentleman
现在	xiànzài	now
笑	xiào	laugh
小	xiǎo	small
小声	xiǎoshēng	whisper
小时	xiǎoshí	hour
小事	xiǎoshì	trifle
消失	xiāoshī	to disappear
消息	xiāoxī	news
小心	xiǎoxīn	careful
夏天	xiàtiān	summer
谢	xiè	to thank
些	xiē	some
谢谢	xièxiè	thank you
蝎子	xiēzi	scorpion
喜欢	xǐhuān	like
姓	xìng	surname
醒(来)	xǐng (lái)	to wake up
行李	xínglǐ	baggage
行星	xíngxīng	planet
星星	xīngxīng	star
行走	xíngzǒu	to walk
兄弟	xiōngdì	brother
休息	xiūxí	to rest
希望	xīwàng	to hope
许多	xǔduō	many
许可	xǔkě	permission, license
需要	xūyào	need
牙	yá	tooth
沿	yán	along

盐	yán	salt
眼(睛)	yǎn (jīng)	eye
阳	yáng	masculine principle in Taoism
样子	yàngzi	to look like, appearance
摇	yáo	to shake or twist
要	yào	to want
咬	yǎo	to bite, to sting
要饭	yàofàn	to beg for food
妖怪	yāoguài	monster
要求	yāoqiú	to request
夜	yè	night
页	yè	page
也	yě	and also
夜叉	yèchā	yaksha
爷爷	yéye	grandfather
一	yī	one
衣(服)	yī (fu)	clothes
一次	yícì	once
一点	yìdiǎn	a little
一定	yídìng	must
一个人	yígè rén	alone
以后	yǐhòu	after
一会儿	yīhuǐ'er	a while
意见	yìjiàn	opinion
已经	yǐjīng	already
音	yīn	sound
银(子)	yín (zi)	silver
赢	yíng	win
应该	yīnggāi	should
影响	yǐngxiǎng	influence

因为	yīnwèi	because
一起	yìqǐ	together
以前	yǐqián	before
一切	yíqiè	all
一生	yìshēng	lifetime
意思	yìsi	meaning
以为	yǐwéi	to think, to believe
一样	yíyàng	same
一直	yìzhí	always, continuously
用	yòng	to use
永远不会	yǒngyuǎn bú huì	will never
游	yóu	journey
又	yòu	again
有	yǒu	to have
游人	yóurén	traveler, tourist
有人	yǒurén	someone
语	yǔ	words, language
遇(到)	yù (dào)	encounter, meet
远	yuǎn	far
原谅	yuánliàng	to forgive
愿意	yuànyì	willing
雨点	yǔdiǎn	raindrops
月(亮)	yuè (liang)	moon
遇见	yùjiàn	to meet
云	yún	cloud
运气	yùnqì	luck
砸	zá	to smash
再	zài	again
在	zài	in, at

在我看来	zài wǒ kàn lái	in my opinion
早晨	zǎochén	morning
造成	zàochéng	cause
怎么	zěnme	how
怎样	zěnyàng	how
站	zhàn	to stand
战斗	zhàndòu	fighting
长	zhǎng	to grow
张	zhāng	(measure word for pages, flat objects)
章	zhāng	chapter
张	zhāng	open
照	zhào	according to, to reflect
找	zhǎo	to search for
照顾	zhàogù	to take care of
着	zhe	(indicates action in progress)
这	zhè	this
这里	zhèlǐ	here
这么	zhème	so
针	zhēn	needle
真	zhēn	true, real
正	zhèng	correct, just
整	zhěng	all
正(在)	zhèng (zài)	(-ing)
争论	zhēnglùn	to argue
真是	zhēnshi	really
真相	zhēnxiàng	the truth
这样	zhèyàng	such
只	zhǐ	only
纸	zhǐ	paper

指	zhǐ	to point at
只	zhī	(measure word for animals)
知(道)	zhī (dào)	knowledge
智(慧)	zhì (huì)	wisdom
直到	zhídào	until
之前	zhīqián	prior to
知识	zhīshì	knowledge
众	zhòng	a crowd
重	zhòng	heavy, hard
种	zhǒng	(measure word for kinds of creatures, things, plants)
钟	zhōng	bell
中	zhōng	in, middle
中间	zhōngjiān	middle
终于	zhōngyú	at last
竹	zhú	bamboo
住	zhù	live
煮	zhǔ	to cook
猪	zhū	pig
抓(住)	zhuā (zhù)	to arrest, to grab
转身	zhuǎnshēn	turn around
转向	zhuǎnxiàng	turn to
追	zhuī	to chase
准备	zhǔnbèi	prepare
桌(子)	zhuō (zi)	table
主意	zhǔyì	idea, plan, decision
字	zì	written character
紫(色)	zǐ (sè)	purple
自己	zìjǐ	oneself
仔细	zǐxì	careful

棕(色)	zōng (sè)	brown
走	zǒu	to go, to walk
走近	zǒu jìn	to approach
钻石	zuànshí	diamond
最	zuì	the most
嘴	zuǐ	mouth
最后	zuìhòu	last, at last
座	zuò	(measure word for mountains, temples, big houses, ...)
做	zuò	to do
坐	zuò	to sit
昨天	zuótiān	yesterday
左右	zuǒyòu	approximately
阻止	zǔzhǐ	to stop, to prevent

About the Authors

Jeff Pepper (author) is President and CEO of Imagin8 Press, and has written dozens of books about Chinese language and culture. Over his thirty-five year career he has founded and led several successful computer software firms, including one that became a publicly traded company. He's authored two software related books and was awarded three U.S. patents.

Dr. Xiao Hui Wang (translator) has an M.S. in Information Science, an M.D. in Medicine, a Ph.D. in Neurobiology and Neuroscience, and 25 years experience in academic and clinical research. She has taught Chinese for over 10 years and has extensive experience in translating Chinese to English and English to Chinese.

Printed in Great Britain
by Amazon

84086317R00098